**Download the
slide deck presentation**

heartland.org/_template-assets/
documents/Books/CAAG-
SlideDeck-2022.pdf

**Download the
digital version**

heartland.org/_template-
assets/documents/Books/
CaaG-2022.pdf

Climate at a Glance for Teachers and Students

Facts on
30 Prominent
Climate Topics

Authored by Anthony Watts & James Taylor

Section 1
The Atmosphere and Land

Crop Production

As the climate has modestly warmed, U.S. crop yields have set new records almost every year. The same is true for nearly all other nations, too. Thanks in large part to longer growing seasons, fewer frost events, more precipitation, and the fertilization effect of atmospheric carbon dioxide, farmers are producing greater amounts of food on fewer acres of land, allowing them to feed the world's growing population.

The 2019 global crop year brought record production of staple cereal crops, such as of corn, rice, and wheat.[3] (See Figure 1.) Further, prior to 2019, crop production records of staple cereal crops were set nearly every year during the previous decade.

Even more remarkable, since 2015, almost every important U.S. crop has set a record for yield per acre, according to the U.S. Department of Agriculture (USDA).[4] For example, USDA reports the three highest records for corn yields occurred in 2017, 2018, and 2019. Further, the five highest rice yields ever recorded occurred from 2015 through 2019, and the wheat yields recorded from 2011 to 2019 are among the top 10 highest wheat yields in U.S. history.

These trends continued throughout the world in 2020. The U.N. Food and Agriculture Organization reported in

Key Takeaways

- Global crop yields have set new records almost every year as our planet has modestly warmed.[1]

- U.S. crop yields have continued to grow, setting new records nearly every year.[2]

- Longer growing seasons, higher temperatures, and greater concentrations of atmospheric carbon dioxide are creating ideal crop conditions.

December 2020 that annual global cereal production increased by 1.3 percent compared to 2019, despite production constraints caused by the COVID-19 pandemic.[5]

Global warming lengthens growing seasons, reduces frost events, and makes more land conducive for crop production. Global soil moisture has maintained pace or improved as the average global temperature has risen modestly in recent decades, with greater oceanic evaporation leading to more precipitation, especially during the summer and fall crop seasons.[6]

Moreover, carbon dioxide greatly benefits crop production, as atmospheric carbon dioxide works as an aerial fertilizer. Higher atmospheric carbon dioxide levels assist plant growth and resistance to drought. It is for this reason that greenhouse operators often pump additional carbon dioxide into their facilities.

Figure 1. Cereal Production, Utilization, and Stocks

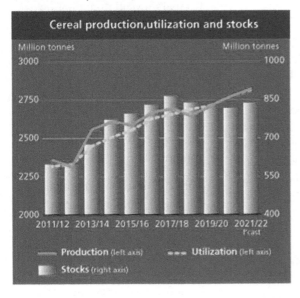

Figure 1. Cereal production, utilization, and stocks. *Source:* U.N. Food and Agriculture Organization, "World Food Situation," fao. org, July 8, 2021, accessed July 25, 2021, http://www.fao.org/worldfoodsituation/csdb/en

References:

1. U.N. Food and Agriculture Organization, "World Food Situation," fao.org, March 12, 2020, **http://www.fao.org/worldfoodsituation/csdb/en**

2. National Agricultural Statistics Service, *Crop Production Historical Track Records*, U.S. Department of Agriculture, April 2019, **https://www.nass.usda.gov/Publications/Todays_Reports/reports/croptr19.pdf**

3. *Ibid.*

4. National Agricultural Statistics Service, *Crop Production Historical Track Records*, U.S. Department of Agriculture, April 2021, **https://www.nass.usda.gov/Publications/Todays_Reports/reports/croptr21.pdf**

5. U.N. Food and Agriculture Organization, "Crop Prospects and Food Situation," *Quarterly Global Report*, No. 4, December 2020, **http://www.fao.org/3/cb2334en/CB2334EN.pdf**

6. Justin Sheffield and Eric F. Wood, "Global Trends and Variability in Soil Moisture and Drought Characteristics, 1950–2000, from Observation-Driven Simulations of the Terrestrial Hydrologic Cycle," *Journal of Climate*, February 1, 2008, pp. 432–458, **https://doi.org/10.1175/2007JCLI1822.1**

Drought

Real-world data show drought conditions in the United States have become less frequent and less severe as the climate has modestly warmed. Moreover, the United Nations reports "low confidence" there are negative trends globally. Droughts have always occurred, and they always will. The available evidence shows the droughts that have occurred in recent years were not caused or worsened by global warming. Instead, global and U.S. drought data show recent droughts were less frequent and severe than the droughts of the early and mid-twentieth century.

The U.S. National Oceanic and Atmospheric Administration data displayed in Figure 1 show that the United States is undergoing its longest period in recorded history without at least 40 percent of the country experiencing "very dry" conditions.[3] Further, it's important to note that the peaks in drought displayed in Figure 1, occurring around 1900, 1930, 1954, and 1978, are much higher than those experienced in the United States in the twentieth and twenty-first centuries.

Key Takeaways

- The United States has benefited from additional precipitation and a reduction in drought conditions as the climate has modestly warmed.

- The United States set records in 2017 and 2019 for having its smallest percentage of land area experiencing drought conditions.[1]

- The U.N. Intergovernmental Panel on Climate Change (IPCC) reports with "high confidence" that precipitation has increased over mid-latitude land areas of the Northern Hemisphere (including the United States) during the past 70 years, while IPCC has "low confidence" there are negative trends globally.[2]

Figure 1. Percentage of the United States Experiencing 'Very Wet' or 'Very Dry' Conditions

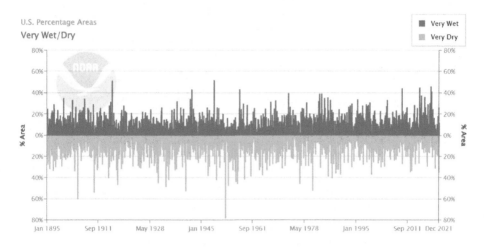

Figure 1. Percentage of United States experiencing "very wet" (in green) or "very dry" (in yellow) conditions. *Source*: National Centers for Environmental Information, "U.S. Percentage Areas (Very Warm/Cold, Very Wet/Dry)," U.S. National Oceanic and Atmospheric Administration, accessed February 1, 2022.

References:

1. Jonathan Erdman, "Drought Coverage in the Continental U.S. Drops to a 21st Century Record Low," weather.com, April 12, 2019, **https://weather.com/news/climate/news/2019-04-12-drought-record-low-coverage-continental-us-april-2019**

2. U.N. Intergovernmental Panel on Climate Change, "Impacts of 1.5°C of Global Warming on Natural and Human Systems," Chapter 3, *Special Report on Global Warming*, 2019, p. 191, **https://www.ipcc.ch/site/assets/uploads/sites/2/2019/06/SR15_Chapter3_Low_Res.pdf**

3. National Centers for Environmental Information, "U.S. Percentage Areas (Very Warm/Cold, Very Wet/Dry)," U.S. National Oceanic and Atmospheric Administration, accessed December 28, 2020, **https://www.ncdc.noaa.gov/temp-and-precip/uspa/wet-dry/0**

Floods

Occasional heavy precipitation events and floods have always occurred and always will. The IPCC reports it has "low confidence" climate change has had a measurable impact on flooding. Moreover, IPCC acknowledges that climate change is as likely to have reduced flooding as it is to have made flooding events more common. When climate activists point to a particular flooding event and claim climate change is to blame, the assertion defies objective data and even the IPCC's own analyses.

Predictions of future flooding are merely that, speculative predictions. Those who claim flooding events *could* increase in the future do so in contradiction to real-world data. Additionally, if any increase in flooding were to occur in the near future, that increase would need to be considered alongside real-world reductions in drought reported by the U.S. National Oceanic and Atmospheric Administration (NOAA).

As Figure 1 shows, NOAA has documented a significant reduction in the costs associated with flooding in the United States over the past century. In the 2018 *National Climate Assessment* published by NOAA, it is stated on page 99, "Human-induced warming has not been formally identified as a factor in increased riverine flooding and the timing of any emergence of a future detectable human caused change is unclear."

Key Takeaways

- The U.N. Intergovernmental Panel on Climate Change (IPCC) reports it has "low confidence" climate change is impacting flooding.

- The IPCC admits having "low confidence" in even the "sign" of any changes. In other words, it is just as likely that climate change is making floods less frequent and less severe as it is more frequent and more severe.[1]

- Studies of rivers and streams that have not been altered by human development show very little, if any, increase in flooding events.

- Floods always have and always will occur. With no increase in overall flooding activity, there is no justifiable reason to blame any recent, current, or near-future flooding event on climate change.

According to a study on the potential of climate-change-related impacts on flooding in the United States and Europe, published in the *Journal of Hydrology*, "The number of significant [flooding] trends was about the number expected due to chance alone. ... The results of this study, for North America and Europe, provide a firmer foundation and support the conclusion of the IPCC that compelling evidence for increased flooding at a global scale is lacking."[2]

Further, a 2014 study titled "Flood Risk and Climate Change: Global and Regional Perspectives,"[3] published in the *Hydrological Sciences Journal*, examined claims in the IPCC's *Fifth Assessment Report* and concluded that "presently we have only low confidence in numerical projections of changes in flood magnitude or frequency resulting from climate change."[4]

Figure 1. Annual Cost of U.S. Flood Damage, 1903–2019

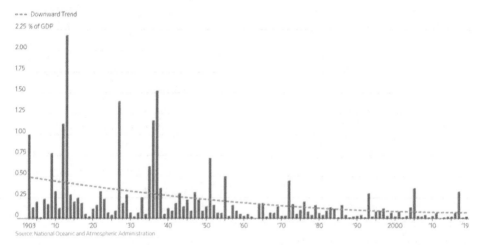

Figure 1. U.S. flood damage as a proportion of U.S. gross domestic product. Data plotted by Bjorn Lomborg. *Data Source*: National Oceanic and Atmospheric Administration.

References:

1. Sonia I. Seneviratne and Neville Nicholls, coordinating lead authors, "Changes in Climate Extremes and Their Impacts on the Natural Physical Environment," Chapter 3, *A Special Report of Working Groups I and II of the Intergovernmental Panel on Climate Change*, Cambridge University Press, pp. 109–230, **https://www.ipcc.ch/site/assets/uploads/2018/03/SREX-Chap3_FINAL-1.pdf**

2. Glenn A. Hodgkins *et al.*, "Climate-Driven Variability in the Occurrence of Major Floods Across North America and Europe," *Journal of Hydrology*, Volume 552, September 2017, pp. 704–717, **http://mural.maynoothuniversity.ie/11682/1/MurphyCo_Climate-driven_2017.pdf**

3. Zbigniew W. Kundzewicz *et al.*, "Flood Risk and Climate Change: Global and Regional Perspectives," *Hydrological Sciences Journal*, Volume 59, Issue 1, 2014, **https://www.tandfonline.com/doi/full/10.1080/02626667.2013.857411**

4. Dennis L. Hartmann, Albert M.G. Klein Tank, and Matilde Rusticucci, coordinating lead authors, "Observations: Atmosphere and Surface: Supplementary Material," Chapter 2, *Climate Change 2013: The Physical Science Basis*, a contribution of Working Group I to the Fifth Assessment Report of the Intergovernmental Panel on Climate Change, 2013, pp. 2SM-1–2SM-26, **http://www.climatechange2013.org/images/report/WG1AR5_Ch02SM_FINAL.pdf**

Snowpack

NASA satellites have measured snow cover since 1966.[1] The lines graphed in Figure 1 represent 12-month snow cover anomalies, which are a departure from a defined reference point. The blue dots represent North American snow cover totals. Note that they show almost no declining trend since 1966, and a rising trend since the late 1980s.[2]

Further, the Eurasian snow data appearing in Figure 1 illustrate there has been a modest decline in Eurasian snow since the 1960s, but that there has also been an increase in snow coverage since the late 1980s.

On a seasonal basis, snowpack throughout the Northern Hemisphere has increased over the past several decades in the fall and winter, as shown in Figures 2 and 3.

As these and other data reveal, the only long-term negative overall snow-cover trends occurring in recent decades have been limited to spring snow cover, primarily in Eurasia. North American snow cover remains approximately the same today as when coverage was first precisely measured in the 1960s, and snow cover has been increasing since the late 1980s.

Key Takeaways

- Average North American snowpack extent is virtually the same as it was in the late 1960s, when U.S. satellite measurements began.

- Following a short-term decline in snowpack in the mid-1980s, average North American snowpack has increased.

- There has been only a modest decline in Eurasian snowpack in recent years.

Figure 1. 12-Month Running Mean Snow Cover Anomalies, November 1966–October 2021

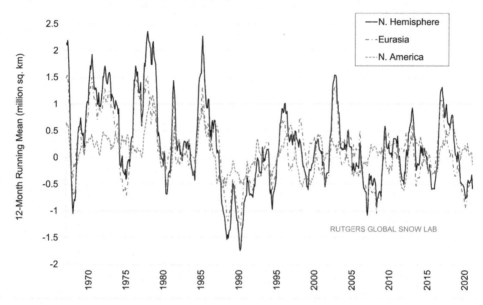

Figure 1. Twelve-month running anomalies of monthly snow extent, from November 1966 to October 2021. Note that North America, represented by the blue dots, remains virtually unchanged in recent years compared to the late 1960s, when satellite measurements first began. *Source*: Global Snow Lab, "12-month Running Anomalies of Monthly Snow Extent from November 1966 to October 2021," Rutgers University Climate Lab, accessed February 2022, https://climate.rutgers.edu/snowcover/chart_anom.php?ui_set=0&ui_region=nhland&ui_month=2

Figure 2. Fall Northern Hemisphere Snow Extent

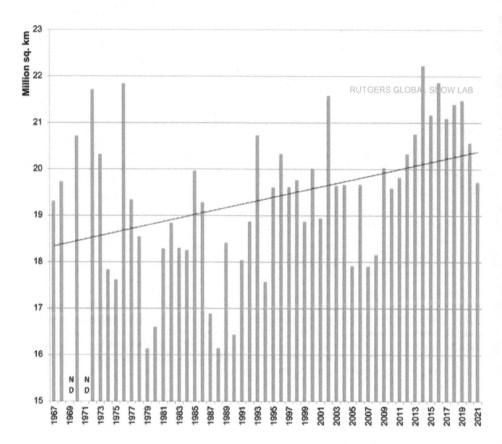

Figure 2. This figure displays fall Northern Hemisphere snow extent. Note that Figure 2 shows that snow cover throughout the Northern Hemisphere has increased during the fall months since the 1960s. (The "ND" in the chart indicates no data for a given year.) *Source*: Global Snow Lab, "Fall Northern Hemisphere Snow Extent," Rutgers University Climate Lab, accessed February 1, 2022, https://climate.rutgers.edu/snowcover/chart_seasonal.php?ui_set=nhland&ui_season=4

Figure 3. Winter Northern Hemisphere Snow Extent

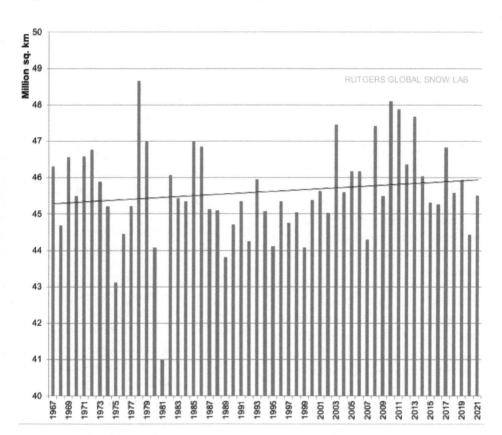

Figure 3. This chart shows winter Northern Hemisphere snow extent. Note that global snow cover throughout the Northern Hemisphere has increased during the winter months since the 1960s. *Source:* Global Snow Lab, "Winter Northern Hemisphere Snow Extent," Rutgers University Climate Lab, accessed February 1, 2022, https://climate.rutgers.edu/snowcover/chart_seasonal.php?ui_set=nhland&ui_season=1

References:

1. See Rutgers University Climate Lab, "Northern Hemisphere Snow and Ice Climate Data Records," accessed February 1, 2022, **https://climate.rutgers.edu/measures/snowice**

2. Global Snow Lab, "12-month Running Anomalies of Monthly Snow Extent from November 1966 to October 2021," Rutgers University Climate Lab, accessed February 1, 2022, **https://climate.rutgers.edu/snowcover/chart_anom.php?ui_set=0&ui_region=nhland&ui_month=2**

Water Levels - Great Lakes

In the early 2010s, during a brief low period for the water levels of the Great Lakes, climate activists repeatedly asserted low water levels were creating a crisis, climate change was to blame for the lower levels, and that water levels would keep falling in the future. For example, in 2013, *Think Progress* claimed, "Several different climate models for the Great Lakes region all predict that lake levels will decline over the next century."[1]

However, since *Think Progress* and others made these dire claims, Great Lakes water marks have reached their highest recorded levels, as shown in Figure 1. Further, the Great Lakes have sustained abundant, above-average water levels since 2014.[2]

In a complete reversal of their previous predictions and warnings, climate activists now claim the high water levels of the Great Lakes are creating a new crisis and that climate change is the cause.[3] Moreover, many have argued that the relative instability of the Great Lakes water levels, which some say is also the result of climate change, is extremely problematic.[4] However, both claims are contradicted by the available scientific evidence and climate activists' prior claims.

High, low, and variable water levels are a longstanding component of the history of the Great Lakes, and as shown in Figure 1, water levels were more volatile in the late 1920s and 1960s than they are today.

Key Takeaways

- The Great Lakes are benefiting from record-high water levels, just a few years after climate activists claimed global warming would cause water levels to drop.

- Water levels have been above average since 2014.

- Many activists now claim global warming causes high water levels, but they have already claimed global warming causes low water levels, calling into question activists' assertion that the science is "settled" on climate change and its consequences.

- Any attempts to claim global warming causes water-level volatility are also contradicted by scientific evidence and the historical record. For example, water levels were more volatile in the late 1920s and the 1960s than they are today.

Figure 1. Great Lakes Water Levels (1918–2020)

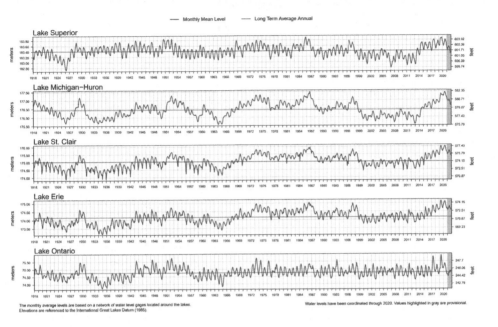

Figure 1. In recent years, Great Lakes water levels have experienced record-high marks, and they have been higher than average since 2014. *Source*: U.S. Army Corps of Engineers, "Great Lakes Water Level Data," accessed February 1, 2022, https://www.lre.usace.army.mil/Missions/Great-Lakes-Information/Great-Lakes-Information-2/Water-Level-Data

References:

1. Matt Kasper, "How Climate Change Is Damaging the Great Lakes, with Implications for the Environment and the Economy," *Think Progress*, January 18, 2013, **https://thinkprogress.org/how-climate-change-is-damaging-the-great-lakes-with-implications-for-the-environment-and-the-economy-ad8a2f5e867d**

2. U.S. Army Corps of Engineers, "Great Lakes Water Level Data," accessed December 2020, **https://www.lre.usace.army.mil/Missions/Great-Lakes-Information/Great-Lakes-Information-2/Water-Level-Data**

3. Kim Frauhammer, "Great Lakes Water Levels Have Swung from Record Lows to Record Highs. Here's Why," *The Washington Post*, November 8, 2019, **https://www.washingtonpost.com/weather/2019/11/08/great-lakes-water-levels-have-swung-record-lows-record-highs-heres-why**

4. Daniel Cusick, "Cities along the Great Lakes Face Rising Water and Costs," *Scientific American*, July 9, 2021, **https://www.scientificamerican.com/article/cities-along-the-great-lakes-face-rising-water-and-costs**

Water Levels-Lake Mead

For most of the past half-century, Lake Mead has enjoyed above-average water levels.[1] Lake Mead water levels rose steadily for 18 years, from 1965 to 1983, and they remained above average for most of the three-decade period from 1973 to 2002. At some point, lower water levels are bound to develop, a reality that is occurring now at Lake Mead.

Relatively lower water levels at Lake Mead are not alarming nor surprising. It is common for regions throughout the world to experience varying periods of lower or higher rainfall and fluctuating water levels. The water levels at Lake Mead are not representative of what has been occurring throughout America over the past 100 years.

As shown in Figure 1, during the past century, much of the continental United States has enjoyed more abundant precipitation as the planet has warmed.[2] Further, the U.N. Intergovernmental Panel on Climate Change (IPCC) has confirmed that since 1951 there has been an *increase* in precipitation in mid-latitude global regions, including the United States, with no detected global precipitation decline.[3]

It is also important to note the Lake Mead reservoir serves water to

Key Takeaways

- Lake Mead water levels rose steadily from 1965 to 1983, setting record-high levels in 1983.

- For all but two years of the three decades running from 1973 to 2002, water levels remained above average, the longest such period on record.

- After nearly 30 years of abundance, a decline was bound to eventually occur.

- Rainfall has been below average in recent years in the Colorado River Basin, but above average nationally.

- Some regions of the world are always going to be drier than others, with or without global warming.

Arizona, California, and Nevada. Every one of those states has experienced significant population increases and greater water demands since the reservoir was filled in 1935, an important factor when considering Lake Mead's water levels.[4,5]

Figure 1. Annual Precipitation Trends in the United States, 1895–2020

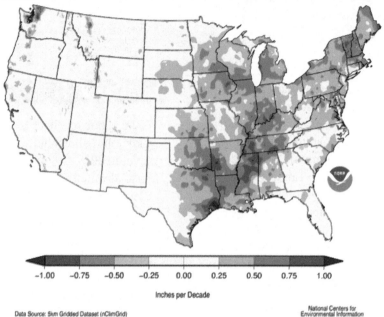

Inches per Decade

Data Source: 5km Gridded Dataset (nClimGrid)

National Centers for
Environmental Information

Figure 1. This figure shows U.S. precipitation trends during the 1895–2020 period. Note that precipitation has increased throughout much of the United States during the past century as the planet has warmed, contradicting claims made by many climate activists insisting that global warming is causing droughts and severe drops in water levels. Also note that the Western United States, shown in grey in Figure 1, has not experienced a strong trend during the studied period. *Source:* National Centers for Environmental Information, "United States Precipitation Trends 1895–2020," National Oceanic and Atmospheric Administration, accessed July 12, 2021, https://www.ncdc.noaa.gov/monitoring-content/temp-and-precip/us-trends/prcp/trends-prcp-ann-por-full.gif

References:

1. Data from U.S. Bureau of Reclamation, "Lake Mead Water Levels — Historical and Current 1935 to the Present," https://usbr.gov/lc/region/g4000/hourly/mead-elv.html. Graphed online by Paul Lutus, accessed December 2020, **https://arachnoid.com/NaturalResources/image.php?mead**

2. National Centers for Environmental Information, "United States Precipitation Trends 1895–2019," National Oceanic and Atmospheric Administration, accessed December 2020, **https://www.ncdc.noaa.gov/monitoring-content/temp-and-precip/us-trends/prcp/trends-prcp-ann-por-full.gif**

3. Ove Hoegh-Guldberg, Daniela Jacob, and Michael Taylor, coordinating lead authors, "Impacts of 1.5°C of Global Warming on Natural and Human Systems," Chapter 3, *Special Report: Global Warming of 1.5 °C*, U.N. Intergovernmental Panel on Climate Change, 2018, p. 191 **https://www.ipcc.ch/site/assets/uploads/sites/2/2019/06/SR15_Chapter3_Low_Res.pdf**

4. U.S Census Bureau, "2020 Census: Percent Change in Resident Population for the 50 States, the District of Columbia, and Puerto Rico: 2010 to 2020," census.gov, accessed July 26, 2021, **https://www.census.gov/library/visualizations/2021/dec/2020-percent-change-map.html**

5. National Park Service, "Overview of Lake Mead," nps.gov, accessed July 26, 2021, **https://www.nps.gov/lake/learn/nature/overview-of-lake-mead.htm**

Water Levels - Lake Tahoe

In 2015 and 2016, climate activists frequently asserted that the 2015–16 California drought, as well as the low water levels at Lake Tahoe allegedly tied to that drought, signaled a "new normal."[1, 2] Since then, however, Lake Tahoe's water level reached its maximum allowable limit of nine feet above gage height (6,229 feet elevation) in 2017, 2018, and 2019, requiring special water releases into the Truckee River.[3] (This is shown clearly in Figure 1.)

It's also worth noting that at the time this book was written, in 2021, California and Lake Tahoe were once again facing a drought. Yet, government officials continued to make water releases into the Truckee River to alleviate Lake Tahoe's high water level.[4]

The failed predictions about Lake Tahoe's water levels provides an excellent illustration of how climate activists use singular events to erroneously make arguments about the dangers of climate change. In the case of the 2015–16 drought affecting Lake Tahoe, climate activists claimed a normal, variable event like a brief drought offered proof of a permanent climate emergency. However, within just a few years of making that dire prediction, they were proven wrong by real-world data.

Key Takeaways

- Lake Tahoe reached its maximum allowable water level in 2017–19, requiring special water releases into the Truckee River.

- The 2015–16 Northern California drought was very brief and followed by three consecutive years of abundant precipitation. During that period, Lake Tahoe reached its maximum allowable water level.

- Activists claiming the 2015–16 drought signaled a "new normal" of drought and low water levels caused by climate change have been proven wrong.

Figure 1. Lake Tahoe Water Levels

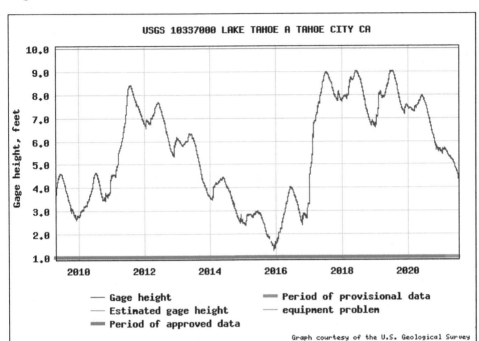

Figure 1. Note that Lake Tahoe reached its maximum allowable water limit in 2017, 2018, and 2019.
Source: U.S. Geological Survey, "USGS 10337000 Lake Tahoe A Tahoe City CA," U.S. Geological Survey, National Water Information System, Accessed July 24, 2021, https://nwis.waterdata.usgs.gov/nwisweb/graph?agency_cd=USGS&site_no=10337000&parm_cd=00065&period=4478

References:

1. Benjamin Spillman, "The 'New Normal'? Sierra Snow Drought Endures Despite 'Miracle' March," *Reno Gazette-Journal*, April 16, 2018, **https://www.rgj.com/story/life/outdoors/2018/04/16/new-normal-sierra-snow-drought-endures-despite-miracle-march/513227002**

2. Center for Watershed Sciences, "Is California's Drought a 'New Normal'?," University of California at Davis, July 15, 2015, **https://californiawaterblog.com/2015/07/15/is-californias-drought-a-new-normal**

3. U.S. Geological Survey, "USGS 10337000 Lake Tahoe A Tahoe City CA," U.S. Geological Survey, National Water Information System, accessed July 24, 2021, **https://nwis.waterdata.usgs.gov/nwisweb/graph?agency_cd=USGS&site_no=10337000&parm_cd=00065&period=4478**

4. Laney Griffo, "Drought Measures: Lake Tahoe Water Released to Meet Goals Downstream," *Tahoe Daily Tribune*, June 11, 2021, accessed July 26, 2021, **https://www.tahoedailytribune.com/news/drought-measures-lake-tahoe-water-released-to-meet-goals-downstream**

Section 2
The Sea and Ice

Coral Reefs

Corals have existed continuously for the past 40 million years.[1] Corals requires warm water, not cold water, to live. Corals cannot survive outside of tropical or subtropical waters. (See Figure 1.)

The primary reasons for coral bleaching events, which vary significantly depending on the time and location, include sediment and fertilizer pollution from nearby coastal lands, chemicals found in sunscreen (oxybenzone), fertilizer and nitrogen loading from agriculture, and cold temperature events.[2,3,4,5]

The argument that corals are being decimated by man-created carbon dioxide emissions is easily disproven by the available data. Coral survived, and even thrived, when global temperatures were significantly higher than they are today.[6] Short-term strong heat waves or cold snaps can cause bleaching events, but such events have occurred many times in history, including long before humans started producing substantial amounts of carbon dioxide emissions. Moreover, studies show coral can and do adapt genetically, and that they are growing increasingly poleward as earth experiences gradual long-term global warming.[7,8]

Further, history shows that cold snaps can harm corals much more than warm spells. In 2010, lower-than-usual ocean temperatures off the coast of Florida killed more corals than any

Key Takeaways

- Corals thrive in warm water, not cold water.

- Recent warming has allowed corals to expand their range poleward while still thriving near the equator.

- Corals have existed continuously for the past 40 million years, surviving temperatures and carbon dioxide levels significantly higher than what is occurring today.

- The primary causes of coral bleaching, which vary based on the time and location, include oxybenzone (a chemical found in sunscreen), sediment runoff from nearby coastal lands, fertilizer and nitrogen loading from agriculture, and lower temperatures like those recorded in 2010 off the Florida coast.

warm-water event, destroying more than 40 percent of reef-building corals in the area.[9]

According to the National Oceanic Atmospheric Administration, "The majority of reef building corals are found within tropical and subtropical

Figure 1. Coral Reef Locations Worldwide

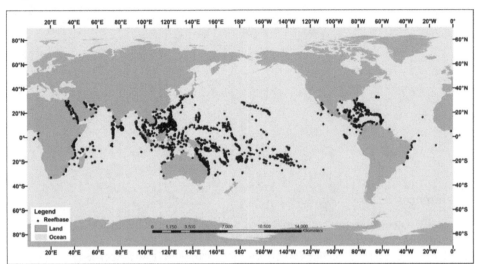

Figure 1. Corals thrive in the warmest of Earth's waters. *Source*: National Ocean Service, "Where Reef Building Corals Found," National Oceanic and Atmospheric Administration, accessed July 26, 2021, https://oceanservice.noaa.gov/education/tutorial_corals/media/supp_coral05a.html

waters. These typically occur between 30^0 north and 30^0 south latitudes. The red dots on this map show the location of major stony coral reefs of the world."[10]

Additionally, many of the stories concerning coral bleaching are not accurate and/or overestimate the problem. For example, the poster child for coral activism is the Great Barrier Reef in Australia. The Australian Institute of Marine Science documented that approximately 22 percent of the Great Barrier Reef experienced bleaching recently, not 93 percent, as reported in some erroneous media stories.[11,12]

Perhaps most importantly, recent evidence shows much of the bleached corals in the Great Barrier Reef are fully recovering. A study by Peter Ridd revealed that not only are the coral at the Great Barrier Reef recovering, the amount of healthy corals is now at an all-time high.[13]

References:

1. Global Reef Project, "Coral Reef History," accessed July 26, 2021, **http://globalreefproject.com/coral-reef-history.php**

2. Zenaida Kotala, "Lathering Up with Sunscreen May Protect Against Cancer – Killing Coral Reefs," *UCF Today*, University of Central Florida, October 20, 2015, **https://www.ucf.edu/news/lathering-up-with-sunscreen-may-protect-against-cancer-killing-coral-reefs-worldwide**

3. D. Lirman *et al.*, "Severe 2010 Cold-Water Event Caused Unprecedented Mortality to Corals of the Florida Reef Tract and Reversed Previous Survivorship Patterns," *PLOS ONE*, Volume 6, Issue 8, August 10, 2011, **https://doi.org/10.1371/journal.pone.0023047**

4. National Oceanic and Atmospheric Administration, "How Pollution Affects Coral Reefs," accessed July 30, 2021, **https://celebrating200years.noaa.gov/visions/coral/side.html**

5. National Ocean Service, "How Does Land-Based Pollution Threaten Coral Reefs?," National Oceanic and Atmospheric Administration, accessed July 26, 2021, **https://oceanservice.noaa.gov/facts/coral-pollution.html**

6. Hiroya Yamano, Kaoru Sugihara, and Keiichi Nomura, "Rapid Poleward Range Expansion of Tropical Reef Corals in Response to Rising Sea Surface Temperatures," *Geophysical Research Letters*, February 17, 2011, **https://doi.org/10.1029/2010GL046474**

7. David Polly, "The Eocene Epoch," University of California Museum of Paleontology Online Exhibit, accessed July 26, 2021, **https://ucmp.berkeley.edu/tertiary/eocene.php**

8. Mikhail Matz *et al.*, "Potential and Limits for Rapid Genetic Adaptation to Warming in a Great Barrier Reef Coral," *PLOS Genetics*, Volume 14, Issue 4, April 19, 2018, **https://doi.org/10.1371/journal.pgen.1007220**

9. D. Lirman *et al., supra* note 3.

10. National Ocean Service, "Where Reef Building Corals Found," National Oceanic and Atmospheric Administration, accessed July 26, 2021, **https://oceanservice.noaa.gov/education/tutorial_corals/media/supp_coral05a.html**

11. Brian Kahn, "Bleaching Hits 93 Percent of the Great Barrier Reef," *Scientific American*, April 20, 2016, accessed July 26, 2021, **https://www.scientificamerican.com/article/bleaching-hits-93-percent-of-the-great-barrier-reef**

12. Michael Slezak, "Agencies Say 22% of Barrier Reef Coral Is Dead, Correcting 'Misinterpretation,'" *The Guardian* (U.K.), June 3, 2016, **https://www.theguardian.com/environment/2016/jun/03/agencies-say-22-of-barrier-reef-coral-is-dead-correcting-misinterpretation**

13. Peter Ridd, "Record Coral Cover of Great Barrier Reef Shames Climate Alarmists," Global Warming Policy Forum, July 23, 2021, **https://www.thegwpf.com/peter-ridd-record-coral-cover-of-great-barrier-reef-refutes-climate-alarmists**

Greenland Ice Melt

S ea-level measurements contradict claims that the loss of ice in the Greenland ice sheet threatens to cause global coastal flooding. NASA satellite images, which include readings dating back to 1993, show sea levels rising at a pace of merely 1.2 inches per decade, which is not significantly different than the typical rate of sea-level rise recorded since the mid-1800s.[1]

Over the past couple of decades, claims of ice melt in Greenland have been used to bolster fears of runaway sea-level rise. For example, NASA scientists said the following about the Greenland and Antarctic ice sheets: "The two regions have lost 6.4 trillion tons of ice in three decades; unabated, this rate of melting could cause flooding that affects hundreds of millions of people by 2100."[2,3]

Although several trillion tons of ice sounds like massive ice loss, it amounts to less than 1 percent of Greenland's total ice mass. As shown in Figure 1, the total ice loss each year is nearly undetectable, coming in at just 0.005 percent of the Greenland ice sheet.

Similarly, on July 30, 2021, media outlets touted scary headlines such as, "Greenland: Enough Ice Melted on Single Day to Cover Florida in Two Inches of Water."[5] While that might sound troubling, data show this amount of ice melt is not unheard of in Greenland, where temperatures are known

Key Takeaways

- Climate activists, including government bureaucrats, claim the Greenland ice sheet is melting six times faster than it was 30 years ago, but 30 years ago, the Greenland ice sheet was barely melting at all. Six times almost no ice loss is hardly an example of a climate change crisis.

- When recent ice loss is compared to the full Greenland ice sheet, the loss is so miniscule that it is practically undetectable.

to rise above freezing on particularly sunny days, melting a large amount of surface ice in a short span. It's an event that has happened many times before, including as recently as 2012.[6]

It is also important to note that pooled meltwater typically refreezes, resulting in virtually no net loss of ice in Greenland's ice sheet. Greenland experienced some melt events in the summer of 2021, driven by abnormally sunny weather, but the melt events were quickly followed by refreezing and a return to normal ice levels within a few days.

Of course, you need not take our word for it. The National Snow and Ice Data

Center wrote of the recent events: "The Greenland Ice Sheet had two extensive melt events in the second half of July. The second melt event had the sixth-largest melt area and fourth-highest runoff in the satellite record, which began in 1978. However, snow cover from earlier snowfall in early summer blunted the potential impact of the melting by limiting the exposure of bare ice and reducing runoff. The two events resulted in the 2021 season flipping from a net gain of ice to near-average net change."[7]

A full-context examination of the data shows only a tiny fraction of Greenland's ice sheet is melting, and with very little impact—the exact opposite of what many climate activists claim.

Figure 1. The Media vs. Reality

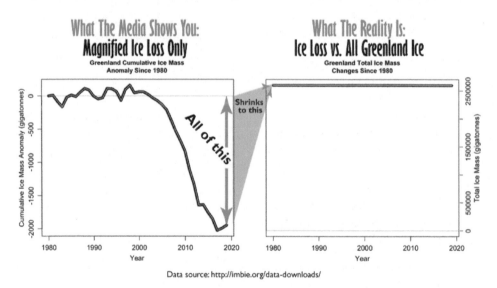

Figure 1. A comparison of presentations of satellite data capturing Greenland's ice mass loss. The image on the right shows changes in Greenland's ice mass relative to Greenland's total ice mass. *Sources:* The data plotted in these graphs are from the Ice Sheet Mass Balance Inter-Comparison Exercise, a joint exercise by NASA and the European Space Agency.[4] Graphs originally by Willis Eschenbach. Adapted and annotated by Anthony Watts.

References:

1. NASA satellite instruments, with readings dating back to 1993, show global sea levels rising at a pace of merely 1.2 inches per decade. See "Sea Level Rise," *Climate at a Glance*, accessed September 6, 2021, **https://climateataglance.com/climate-at-a-glance-sea-level-rise**

2. See NASA, "Greenland, Antarctica Melting Six Times Faster Than in the 1990s," press release, nasa.gov, last updated March 18, 2020, **https://www.nasa.gov/feature/jpl/greenland-antarctica-melting-six-times-faster-than-in-the-1990s**

3. Brandon Specktor, "Ice loss in Antarctica and Greenland Increased Sixfold in the Last 30 Years," *LiveScience*, March 13, 2020, **https://www.livescience.com/antarctica-greenland-ice-shelf-loss.html**

4. Ice Sheet Mass Balance Inter-Comparison Exercise, "About IMBIE," NASA and the European Space Agency, imbie.org, accessed September 5, 2021, **http://imbie.org/about-the-project**

5. Oliver Milman, "Greenland: Enough Ice Melted on Single Day to Cover Florida in Two Inches of Water," *The Guardian* (U.K.), July 30, 2021, **https://www.theguardian.com/environment/2021/jul/30/greenland-ice-sheet-florida-water-climate-crisis**

6. Mark Hobson, "Thin Clouds Drove Greenland's Record-Breaking 2012 Ice Melt," University of Wisconsin at Madison, April 3, 2013, **https://news.wisc.edu/thin-clouds-drove-greenlands-record-breaking-2012-ice-melt**

7. National Snow and Ice Data Center, "Large Melt Events Change the Story of 2021, Published August 11, 2021," August 11, 2021, **http://nsidc.org/greenland-today/2021/08/large-melt-event-changes-the-story-of-2021**

Islands and Sea-Level Rise

Climate change activists routinely argue that numerous Pacific Islands will soon be under water due to rising sea levels caused by climate change. But recent population patterns suggest Pacific Islanders know they are not facing substantial threats from sea-level rise. Some allegedly "endangered" islands have even built or made plans to build new airports or resorts.[1,2]

Even more importantly, objective scientific evidence debunks claims that climate change is causing small islands to disappear. Rising seas bring sand and sediment, which build up coastal shorelines, often offsetting higher-than-usual sea levels.

An important example is the island of Tuvalu. Climate activists often claim the island nation of Tuvalu is sinking because of rising seas. However, a recent peer-reviewed study found eight of Tuvalu's nine large coral atolls have grown in size during recent decades, and 75 percent of Tuvalu's 101 smaller reef islands have increased as well.[3]

Further evidence can be found in Tuvalu's population records. Many climate activists have warned that rising seas have started to cause or will soon cause waves of climate refugees seeking to flee islands like Tuvalu. However, Tuvalu's population, like the population of many other island nations, has consistently grown in recent years, not

Key Takeaways

- Most islands and atolls in the Pacific Ocean, including Tuvalu, are increasing in size, not shrinking.

- As the sea gradually rises, it brings sand and sediment along with it, building up island shorelines at a rate that offsets modest sea-level rise.

- Despite many predictions that island nations in the Pacific would spawn waves of climate refugees, the population of Tuvalu and other islands have steadily grown, not decreased.

declined. At the time of this book's publication, the population of Tuvalu had increased by 20 percent over the previous 30 years, and it had doubled compared to its population recorded in 1970.[4]

Additional peer-reviewed studies have confirmed other islands in the Pacific Ocean are keeping up with rising sea levels.[5,6] Their atolls have gained more than enough height and mass to offset modest sea-level rise.[7]

Climate activist groups and some scientists have been making false dire warnings about sea-level rise for many decades. For instance, more than 30 years ago, the *AFP* international news agency reported all 1,196 islands that comprise the Maldives could be completely underwater over the next few decades.[8] Not only are all 1,196 islands still above water, people from all over the world are flocking to the Maldives, not fleeing them. Like Tuvalu, the Maldives are benefiting from a lucrative tourist trade, not spawning climate refugees.

References:

1. Anthony Watts, "FAIL: 30 Year-Old Climate Prediction Proves to Be a Load of Bunkum," *WattsUpWithThat*, March 10, 2018, **https://wattsupwiththat.com/2018/10/03/fail-30-year-old-climate-prediction-proves-to-be-a-load-of-bunkum**

2. Eric Worrall, "Kiribati Climate Plan: More Resorts, More Tourists," *WattsUpWithThat*, November 21, 2017, **https://wattsupwiththat.com/2017/11/21/kirabati-climate-plan-more-resorts-more-tourists**

3. "'Sinking' Pacific Nation Is Getting Bigger: Study," *Phys.org*, February 9, 2018, **https://phys.org/news/2018-02-pacific-nation-bigger.html**

4. "Tuvalu Population," *worldometer.info*, **https://www.worldometers.info/world-population/tuvalu-population**

5. Megan Tuck *et al.*, "Physical Modelling of the Response of Reef Islands to Sea-Level Rise," *Geology*, Volume 47, No. 9, September 1, 2019, **https://pubs.geoscienceworld.org/gsa/geology/article-abstract/47/9/803/572047/Physical-modelling-of-the-response-of-reef-islands?redirectedFrom=fulltext**

6. Paul S. Kench, Murray R. Ford and Susan D. Owen, "Patterns of Island Change and Persistence Offer Alternate Adaptation Pathways for Atoll Nations," *Nature Communications*, February 9, 2018, **https://www.nature.com/articles/s41467-018-02954-1**

7. Willis Eschenbach, "Floating Islands," *WattsUpWithThat*, January 27, 2010, **https://wattsupwiththat.com/2010/01/27/floating-islands/**

8. "Threat to Islands," *AFP*, republished by *Canberra Times* (Australia), September 26, 1988, **https://trove.nla.gov.au/newspaper/article/102074798**

Ocean Acidification

Scientists and media outlets claim ocean acidification is occurring due to increased carbon dioxide (CO_2) levels in the atmosphere,[1] but objective data show the oceans are far from acidic.

A pH of 7 is considered neutral, with anything below 7 considered acidic. Ocean pH averages 8.1, which is alkaline rather than acidic. Climate models suggest the ocean's surface pH may have dropped from pH of 8.2 to 8.1 since 1750, though that change was never actually measured. In reality, the very small pH drop is merely a modeled conjecture.[2]

A study by scientists at the CO2 Coalition notes that the health of ocean life is enhanced by more carbon dioxide, not less.[3] CO2 is food for phytoplankton, which form the foundation of the marine food chain.

As Figure 1 shows, with an average pH of 8.1, the oceans are a long way from turning acidic. It is likely that media reports often use the word "acidic" because it sounds scarier than a more accurate description, such as "a modeled, modest decline in alkalinity."

Key Takeaways

- Ocean water is not overly acidic.

- A pH of 7 is considered neutral. A pH below 7 is acidic. A pH above 7 is alkaline.

- The pH of the oceans averages 8.1, and it ranges from 7.8 to 8.5. By comparison, rainwater is "acidic," averaging 5.6.

- Since 1850, the pH of surface ocean waters has fallen by merely 0.1 pH units.

- The health of ocean life is improved, not harmed, by more carbon dioxide (CO2). CO2 is food for phytoplankton that form the foundation of the marine food chain. Marine life thrives and improves growth rates in elevated CO2 conditions.

Figure 1. The pH Scale

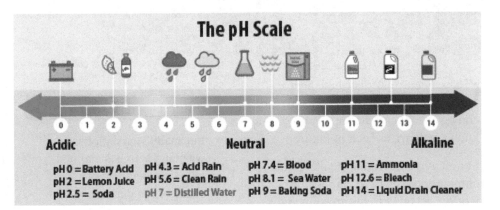

Figure 1. Comparison of the pH of common substances. *Source*: U.S. Environmental Protection Agency, "Measuring Acid Rain," epa.gov, last accessed August 12, 2021, https://www.epa.gov/acidrain/what-acid-rain

References:

1. Pacific Marine Environmental Laboratory, "What is Ocean Acidification?," National Oceanic and Atmospheric Administration, accessed August 12, 2021, **https://www.pmel.noaa.gov/co2/story/What+is+Ocean+Acidification%3F**

2. K. Caldeira and M.E. Wickett, "Ocean Model Predictions of Chemistry Changes from Carbon Dioxide Emissions to the Atmosphere and Ocean," *Journal of Geophysical Research*, Volume 110, September 21, 2005, **https://agupubs.onlinelibrary.wiley.com/doi/10.1029/2004JC002671**

3. CO2 Coalition, *Ocean Health: Is There an 'Acidification' Problem?*, June 2020, accessed August 12, 2021, **http://co2coalition.org/wp-content/uploads/2020/06/Steele-Ocean-Health-White-Paper-final-5-28-20.pdf**

Climate at a Glance
Ocean Currents

Ocean currents distribute heat across the globe. The great ocean conveyor moves water in a well-known pattern, as seen in Figure 1.[1]

For many years, some scientists and climate activists have claimed the world's ocean currents are slowing down and that global warming is to blame. They have cited computer model simulations that predicted and replicated a slowdown.[2] Slower ocean currents, they claimed, would alter African and Indian rainfall patterns and impact Atlantic hurricanes. Additionally, in 2019, op-eds and studies claimed ocean currents had declined to their slowest pace in 1,600 years.[3,4]

However, recent scientific research, relying on real-world measurements, shows ocean currents likely sped up during the same periods that climate activists asserted global warming had started to cause ocean currents to slow.[5] It seems that scientists cannot agree on whether ocean currents are speeding up or slowing down. Either way, the media wants you to believe that human activity is the cause of the change, rather than natural variations in Earth's climate system. Global warming activists cannot have it both ways. Ocean currents could not have been both slowing down to record lows during the past 20 years while also speeding up.

When climate change activists thought ocean currents were slowing down, they told the public this develop-

Key Takeaways

- For many years, global warming activists claimed climate change would soon cause ocean currents to slow to a pace that has not been experienced in more than 1,000 years.

- Climate activists claimed computer models predicted the slowdown and that a slowdown would cause disastrous consequences on marine life.

- They also suggested it could cause a new "mini" ice age.

- However, recent peer-reviewed research has falsified these claims. The best-available science shows ocean currents have sped up over the past 20 years, not slowed down.

ment would be disastrous and that their computer models predicted this would undoubtedly happen due to global warming. Now that we know ocean currents have been speeding up, many of the same activists tell us this change is also disastrous, and that their computer models predicted accelerating ocean currents all along.[6]

It is clear global warming activists are continuously altering their claimed "climate crisis" to fit the evolving scientific evidence, rather than simply admitting the obvious: Earth's climate and ocean currents are always changing and always will, due mostly to natural causes.

Figure 1. Ocean Currents Around the World

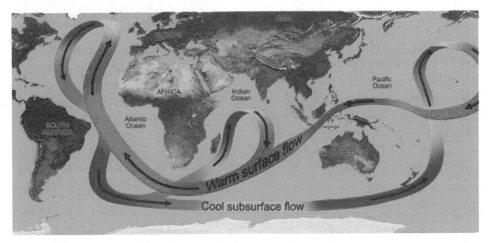

Figure1. This figure illustrates how ocean currents affect heat distribution around the world. *Source*: National Ocean Service, "What Is the Global Ocean Conveyor Belt?," National Oceanic and Atmospheric Administration, last updated February 26, 2021, https://oceanservice.noaa.gov/facts/conveyor.html

References:

1. National Ocean Service, "What Is the Global Ocean Conveyor Belt?," National Oceanic and Atmospheric Administration, last updated February 26, 2021, **https://oceanservice.noaa.gov/facts/conveyor.html**

2. Nancy Bazilchuk, "In Deep Water: Will Essential Ocean Currents be Altered by Climate Change?," *Scientific American*, December 10, 2009, **https://www.scientificamerican.com/article/deep-water-ocean-currents-climate**

3. Aylin Woodward, "The Film 'The Day After Tomorrow' Foretold a Real and Troubling Trend: The Ocean's Water-Circulation System Is Weakening," *Business Insider*, March 25, 2019, **https://www.businessinsider.com/day-after-tomorrow-was-right-and-wrong-about-climate-shifts-2019-3**

4. David Thronalley *et al.*, "Anomalously Weak Labrador Sea Convection and Atlantic Overturning During the Past 150 Years," *Nature*, Volume 556, April 2018, **https://pubmed.ncbi.nlm.nih.gov/29643484/#:~:text=Anomalously%20weak%20Labrador%20Sea%20convection%20and%20Atlantic%20overturning,redistributing%20heat%20and%20influencing%20the%20carbon%20cycle%3Csup%3E1%2C%202%3C%2Fsup%3E**

5. Shijian Hu *et al.*, "Deep-Reaching Acceleration of Global Mean Ocean Circulation Over the Past Two Decades," *Science Advances*, Volume 6, No. 6, February 2020, **https://pubmed.ncbi.nlm.nih.gov/32076640**

6. Stephanie Pappas, "Ocean Currents Are Getting Faster," *Live Science*, February 6, 2020, **https://www.livescience.com/ocean-currents-speeding-up.html**

Sea-Level Rise

Global sea level has risen more than 400 feet since the end of the last ice age glaciation. Global sea levels have been rising at a relatively steady pace of approximately 1 foot per century since at least the mid-1800s.[1] One of the oldest tide-gauge records of sea level, New York City's "Battery," shows a linear trend of 2.88 mm per year (0.113 inches per year) since 1856, with very little, if any, recent acceleration.[2] (See Figure 1.)

A smaller dataset of satellite data going back to 1993 also shows little, if any, acceleration in the pace of sea-level rise.[3]

Perhaps most importantly, an independent analysis of tide-gauge data, which has a much longer record compared to satellite data, found humans have likely had only a very modest impact on long-term sea-level rise. Climatologist Roy Spencer performed the analysis, which is illustrated in Figure 2.

Spencer's analysis suggests humans' contribution to sea-level rise could be as little as three-tenths of an inch per decade, or about three inches per century. Natural sea-level rise accounts for half an inch of sea-level rise per decade, or 5 inches per century. Combined, the rate of sea-level rise is eight-tenths of an inch per decade, or 8 inches per century, which is even slower than what satellite instruments report.

Key Takeaways

- Global sea levels have risen more than 400 feet since the beginning of the interglacial period, and data show they have always risen between ice ages.

- Sea levels have been rising at a fairly steady pace since at least the mid-1800s.

- NASA satellite instruments, with readings dating back to 1993, show global sea levels rising at a pace of merely 1.2 inches per decade.

- Tide gauge data going back to the 1850s show a much lower rate, between 0.8 and 0.9 inches per decade, with no hint of acceleration.

Figure 1. Sea-Level Rise Recorded by the 'Battery' in New York

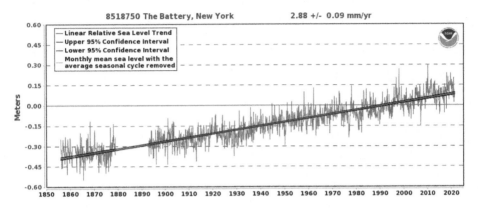

Figure 1. Tidal gauge measurements at the Battery in New York City illustrate there has been a steady, modest pace of sea-level rise of a little more than 1 inch per decade since the 1850s. *Source:* National Oceanic and Atmospheric Administration, "Relative Sea Level Trend, 8518750 The Battery, New York," *Tides and Currents*, tidesandcurrents.noaa.gov, accessed August 13, 2021, https://tidesandcurrents.noaa.gov/sltrends/sltrends_station.shtml?id=8518750

Figure 2. Global Sea-Level Rise, 1880–2013, from Tide-Gauge Data

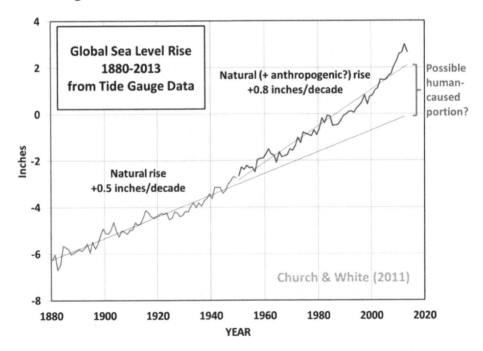

Figure 2. This figure shows sea-level rise dating back to 1880. Graph by Roy Spencer, Ph.D. For a more detailed analysis, see Spencer's article, which can be found in Note 4 in the References section below.

References:

1. U.S. Geological Survey, "How Does Present Glacier Extent and Sea Level Compare to the Extent of Glaciers and Global Sea Level During the Last Glacial Maximum?," usgs. gov, accessed August 16, 2021, **https://www.usgs.gov/faqs/how-does-present-glacier-extent-and-sea-level-compare-extent-glaciers-and-global-sea-level**

2. National Oceanic and Atmospheric Administration, "Relative Sea Level Trend, 8518750 The Battery, New York," *Tides and Currents*, tidesandcurrents.noaa.gov, accessed August 13, 2021, **https://tidesandcurrents.noaa.gov/sltrends/sltrends_station. shtml?id=8518750**

3. Sea Level Research Group, "Global Mean Sea Level (Seasonal Signals Removed)," University of Colorado, sealevel.colorado.edu, last accessed August 15, 2021, **http:// sealevel.colorado.edu**

4. Roy Spencer, "Sea Level Rise: Human Portion Is Small," drroyspencer.com, May 25, 2018, accessed September 7, 2021, **https://www.drroyspencer.com/2018/05/sea-level-rise-human-portion-is-small**

Section 3

Temperature and Extreme Weather

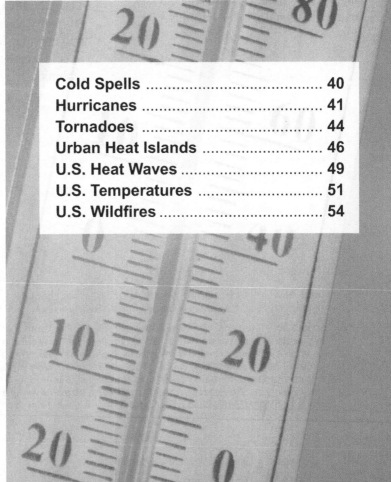

Cold Spells

G lobal warming activists frequently respond to polar vortex
events and other extreme cold weather
events by claiming climate change is
to blame.[1] Not only does blaming cold
weather outbreaks on global warming
defy common sense, it also defies
well-established scientific evidence
and the findings of the U.N. Intergovernmental Panel on Climate Change
(IPCC). The IPCC's 2018 *SREX* report
says it is "very likely" there have been
fewer very cold days and nights in recent decades, and the report's authors
further claim it is "virtually certain"
that there will be "deceases in cold
extremes" due to global warming.[2]

Key Takeaways

- Objective data show global warming has not caused an increase in the frequency or severity of cold weather events.

- The U.N. Intergovernmental Panel on Climate Change reported in 2018 that it is "very likely" that there have been fewer very cold days and nights in recent decades.

- The U.N. IPCC reports it is "virtually certain" that there will continue to be decreases in cold-weather temperature extremes.

References:

1. Justin Rowlatt, "Polar Vortex: What Role Does Climate Change Play?," BBC News, January 31, 2019, **https://www.bbc.com/news/world-us-canada-47078054**

2. Sonia Seneviratne and Neville Nicholls, coordinating lead authors, *et al.*, "Changes in Climate Extremes and their Impacts on the Natural Physical Environment," Chapter 3, *Managing the Risks of Extreme Events and Disasters to Advance Climate Change Adaptation (SREX). A Special Report of Working Groups I and II of the Intergovernmental Panel on Climate Change* (Cambridge, U.K.: Cambridge University Press, 2012), accessed August 14, 2021, **https://www.ipcc.ch/site/assets/uploads/2018/03/SREX-Chap3_FINAL-1.pdf**

Hurricanes

D evastating hurricanes occurred long before the invention of automobiles and coal-fired power plants, and real-world hurricane activity shows little, if any, impact from global warming.

The Intergovernmental Panel on Climate Change (IPCC) has largely agreed with this view. In its 2018 interim report, IPCC stated there is "only low confidence for the attribution of any detectable changes in tropical cyclone activity to anthropogenic influences."[1] Similarly, in the IPCC's AR6 WG1 report, released in August 2021, the IPCC noted, "Identifying past trends in TC [tropical storm] metrics remains a challenge," a statement that essentially admits scientists have yet to identify a solid measurable upward trend in the data.[2]

The IPCC's findings are well supported by objective hurricane and tropical storm data.[3] (See Figure 1.)

Most importantly for Americans, the impacts hurricanes have on the United States are at an all-time low. The United States recently went more than a decade (2005 through 2017) without a major hurricane—a hurricane measuring Category 3 or higher—making landfall. That is the longest such period in recorded history.[3]

The United States also recently experienced the fewest number of hurricane strikes in any eight-year period in recorded history

Key Takeaways

- Many researchers have found there has been no increase in hurricanes as the planet has modestly warmed.

- The U.N. IPCC agrees, finding no increase in the frequency or severity of hurricanes.

- The United States recently went through its longest period in recorded history without a major hurricane strike.

- The United States recently experienced its fewest total hurricanes in any eight-year period.

- Florida, America's most hurricane-prone state, recently underwent its longest period in recorded history without any hurricanes.

(2009 through 2017).[4] Additionally, America's most vulnerable state for hurricanes, Florida, concluded an 11-year period without a landfalling hurricane of any size in 2016, the longest such period in recorded history.[5] The Gulf of Mexico also recently benefited from its longest hurricane-free period in recorded history (2013–16).

Whenever a hurricane forms, global

warming activists claim modestly warmer global ocean temperatures are "supercharging" the storms. However, warm ocean water is just one factor in the formation and intensification of hurricanes. Wind shear inhibits strong storms from forming and rips apart storms that have already formed. This is important to note, because scientists have learned that global warming is likely to cause more wind shear in places where hurricanes form and intensify.[6]

Figure 1. Global Tropical Cyclone Frequency

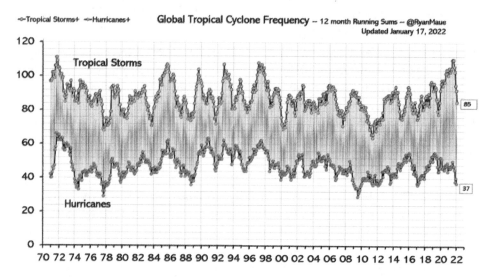

Figure 1. This figure shows that global hurricane and tropical cyclone activity is not increasing. Even with the slight uptick in the number of tropical storms in 2021, it is still below the peak recorded in 1971. Source: Ryan N. Maue, "Global Tropical Cyclone Activity," *Climate Atlas*, accessed February 1, 2022, http://climatlas.com/tropical/frequency_12months.png

References:

1. Sonia Seneviratne and Neville Nicholls, coordinating lead authors, *et al.*, "Changes in Climate Extremes and their Impacts on the Natural Physical Environment," Chapter 3, *Managing the Risks of Extreme Events and Disasters to Advance Climate Change Adaptation (SREX). A Special Report of Working Groups I and II of the Intergovernmental Panel on Climate Change* (Cambridge, U.K.: Cambridge University Press, 2012), accessed August 14, 2021, **https://www.ipcc.ch/site/assets/ uploads/2018/03/SREX-Chap3_FINAL-1.pdf**

2. Sonia I. Seneviratne and Xuebin Zhang, coordinating lead authors, *et al.*, "Weather and Climate Extreme Events in a Changing Climate," Chapter 11, *Climate Change 2021: The Physical Science Basis. A Contribution of Working Group I to the Sixth Assessment Report of the Intergovernmental Panel on Climate Change* (Cambridge, U.K.: Cambridge University Press, in press, August 2021), accessed September 6, 2021, **https://www.ipcc.ch/report/ar6/wg1/downloads/report/IPCC_AR6_WGI_Chapter_11. pdf**

3. Ryan N. Maue, "Global Tropical Cyclone Activity," *Climate Atlas*, accessed February 1, 2022, **http://climatlas.com/tropical/frequency_12months.png**

4. Doyle Rice, "U.S. Experiencing Record Hurricane Drought, Just 4 Strikes in 7 Years," *USA Today*, July 12, 2016, **https://www.usatoday.com/story/weather/2016/07/12/us- hurricane-drought/86990408**

5. Barbara Hollingsworth, "U.S. Hits Record 129 Months Since Last Major Hurricane Strike," *CNS News*, July 15, 2016, **https://www.cnsnews.com/news/article/barbara- hollingsworth/us-hits-record-129-months-last-major-hurricane-strike**

6. University of Miami Rosenstiel School of Marine and Atmospheric Science, "Global Warming Increases Wind Shear, Reduces Hurricanes, Climate Model Shows," *Science Daily*, April 18, 2007, **https://www.sciencedaily.com/releases/2007/04/070417182843. htm**

Tornadoes

Tornadoes typically form when very cold, dry air clashes with warm, humid air. Climate change warms the Arctic more than the tropics and subtropics, resulting in less of a clash between cold Arctic air masses and warm Gulf of Mexico air masses. As a result, fewer and less violent tornadoes are occurring today than in previous periods, despite media claims that tornadoes are getting more frequent, stronger, or both.[1,2]

The number of tornadoes in the United States, as well as in other countries, has been slowly declining for the past 45 years. At the same time, the number of strong to violent tornadoes, EF3 or higher, has been *dramatically* declining for the past 45 years. (See Figure 1.) In fact, the United States set a record in 2017–18 for the longest period in recorded history without a tornado death, and it set a record for the longest period in history (306 days) without an EF3 or stronger tornado.[3,4] The two record-low years for tornado strikes in the United States both occurred this past decade, in 2014 and 2018.[5]

Further, even the alarmist U.N. Intergovernmental Panel on Climate Change has acknowledged, "There is low confidence in observed trends in small spatial-scale phenomena such as tornadoes."[6]

Key Takeaways

- The number of tornadoes in the United States has been declining for the past 45 years.

- The number of strong tornadoes, rated as EF3 or higher, has been dramatically declining for the past 45 years.

- In 2017–18, the United States set a record for the longest period in history without a death caused by a tornado.

- In 2017–18, the United States set a record for the longest period in history without an EF3 or stronger tornado.

- According to a climate report by the United Nations, "There is low confidence in observed trends in small spatial-scale phenomena such as tornadoes."

Figure 1. U.S. Annual Count of Strong to Violent Tornadoes (EF3+), 1970–2020

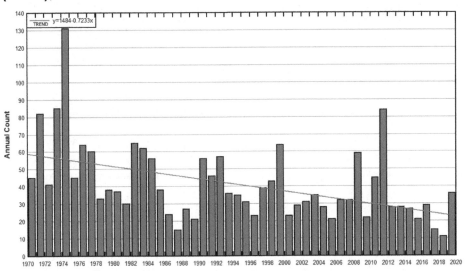

Figure 1. This figure shows the frequency of strong to violent tornadoes (tornadoes registering EF3 or stronger) has been declining since the early 1970s. *Sources*: Graph by Anthony Watts using official NOAA/Storm Prediction Center data.[7,8,9]

References:

1. Nsikan Akpan, "Is Climate Change Making U.S. Tornadoes Worse?," Public Broadcasting Service, March 5, 2019, **https://www.pbs.org/newshour/science/is-climate-change-making-u-s-tornadoes-worse**

2. Bob Berwyn, "Is Climate Change Fueling Tornadoes?," *Inside Climate News*, May 30, 2019, **https://insideclimatenews.org/news/30052019/tornado-climate-change-connection-science-research-data**

3. Doyle Rice, "U.S. Sets Record of 246 Straight Days without a Tornado Death," *USA Today*, January 17, 2018, **https://www.usatoday.com/story/weather/2018/01/17/u-s-sets-record-246-straight-days-without-tornado-death/1041125001**

4. Chris Dolce, "Record-Long Streak With No EF3 or Stronger Tornadoes in the U.S. Ends in Jacksonville, Alabama," The Weather Channel, March 18, 2018, **https://weather.com/storms/tornado/news/2018-03-21-jacksonville-alabama-tornado-ends-ef3-united-states-drought**

5. Doyle Rice, "2018 Was an All-Time Record Quiet Year for Tornadoes in the U.S.," *USA Today*, December 28, 2018, **https://www.usatoday.com/story/news/nation/2018/12/28/tornadoes-set-record-lows-2018-only-10-deaths-us/2431360002**

6. U.N. Intergovernmental Panel on Climate Change, *Changes in Climate Extremes and Their Impacts on the Natural Physical Environment*, Chapter 3, 2018, accessed August 16, 2021, **https://www.ipcc.ch/site/assets/uploads/2018/03/SREX-Chap3_FINAL-1.pdf**

7. National Oceanic and Atmospheric Administration, "Historical Records and Trends," accessed September 1, 2021, **https://www.ncdc.noaa.gov/climate-information/extreme-events/us-tornado-climatology/trends**

8. Daniel McCarthy and Joseph Schaefer, "Tornado Trends over the Past Thirty Years," NOAA, National Weather Service, NWS, NCEP, Storm Prediction Center, accessed 8/16/21, **https://www.spc.noaa.gov/publications/mccarthy/tor30yrs.pdf**

9. Graph data from National Oceanic and Atmospheric Administration's National Weather Service, Storm Prediction Center website, accessed August 16, 2021, **https://www.spc.noaa.gov/wcm**

Urban Heat Islands

The majority of U.S. temperature stations utilized for the National Oceanic and Atmospheric Administration and NASA temperature records have been compromised by the encroachment of artificial surfaces like concrete, asphalt, buildings, and air conditioner exhausts. The effects of these manmade structures are often referred to as urban heat islands. (Figures 1 and 2 provide examples of how temperature stations have been compromised by urbanization.)

Urban heat islands cause temperature data to display higher temperatures than what would have been recorded if the same stations were located away from urban areas. Some researchers have found urban heat islands are responsible for almost half of reported U.S. warming. When only non-urban temperature stations are used, warming trends are still present in the data, depending on the period examined, but they are minimal and not at all alarming.[1]

The data in Figure 3 show temperature stations that have not been corrupted by the urban heat island effect report significantly less warming than temperature stations corrupted by urban heat island impacts.[2] Still, despite this well-known problem, corrupted temperature stations compose a majority of the stations used to report official U.S. temperature data.[3]

Key Takeaways

- Urban heat islands, which grow with the size of cities, create artificial warming at many long-term temperature stations.

- On average, urban heat islands increase the global surface temperature trend by almost 50 percent.

- Nearly 90 percent of U.S. temperature stations have been compromised by urbanization effects.

- About half of the reported U.S. warming effectively disappears in the data when analysts consider only those stations that have not been corrupted by heat islands.

There is also strong evidence of similar siting problems in other parts of the world, including at many official weather stations. This suggests the same urban heat island corruptions that have occurred in U.S. data are also present in data compiled from other countries. Researchers at the Oak Ridge National Laboratory confirmed this theory in important work published in 2019.[5]

Figure 1. Weather Station Used to Gather Climate Data in a Parking Lot at the University of Arizona

Figure 1. U.S. Historical Climatology Network weather station used to collect climate data. This station is located in a parking lot at the University of Arizona in Tucson. The station was previously located in a grassy area, but researchers moved the station as the campus grew. Photo by Anthony Watts.

Figure 2. NOAA Temperature Sensor in Ardmore, Oklahoma

Figure 2. NOAA temperature sensor (used for climate data) located on street corner in Ardmore, Oklahoma. Note that the sensor's data is being corrupted by heating signatures of the nearby building, asphalt, and automobiles. Photo by Anthony Watts.

Figure 3. A Comparison of Corrupted and Uncorrupted Temperature Station Data

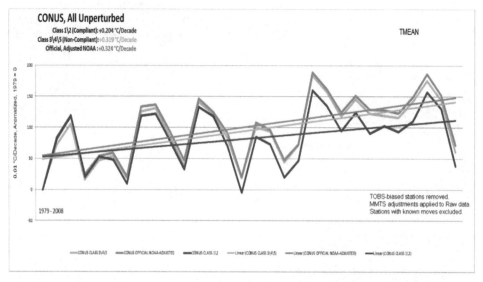

Figure 3. Uncorrupted stations (classes one and two) report much less warming than stations corrupted by urban heat island factors (classes three, four, and five). *Source:* Anthony Watts, *Is the U.S. Surface Temperature Record Reliable?*, The Heartland Institute and SurfaceStations.org, 2009, https://www.heartland.org/_template-assets/documents/publications/SurfaceStations.pdf

References:

1. See Anthony Watts *et al.*, "New Study of NOAA's U.S. Climate Network Shows a Lower 30-Year Temperature Trend When High Quality Temperature Stations Unperturbed by Urbanization Are Considered," press release, American Geophysical Union, December 16, 2015, displaying parts of a presentation delivered before the American Geophysical Union, **https://web.archive.org/web/20160331214630/https://fallmeeting.agu. org/2015/press-item/new-study-of-noaas-u-s-climate-network-shows-a-lower-30-year-temperature-trend-when-high-quality-temperature-stations-unperturbed-by-urbanization-are-considered**

2. Anthony Watts *et al.*, "Comparison of Temperature Trends Using an Unperturbed Subset of the U.S. Historical Climatology Network," poster presentation, American Geophysical Union, December 16, 2015, **https://wattsupwiththat.files.wordpress. com/2015/12/agu-poster-watts-website-release.pdf**

3. See Anthony Watts, *Is the U.S. Surface Temperature Record Reliable?*, The Heartland Institute and SurfaceStations.org, 2009, **https://www.heartland.org/_template-assets/ documents/publications/SurfaceStations.pdf**

4. Ronald D. Leeper *et al.*, "Impacts of Small-Scale Urban Encroachment on Air Temperature Observations," *Journal of the American Meteorological Society*, Volume 58, Issue 6, June 1, 2019, **https://journals.ametsoc.org/doi/10.1175/JAMC-D-19-0002.1**

Climate at a Glance
U.S. Heat Waves

Heat waves have always been a natural part of the climate in much of the United States, and there is no strong evidence that shows global warming is making heat waves more severe or frequent, when put in the proper historical context. The lion's share of the modest warming that has occurred over the past few decades has largely affected winter temperatures, locations closer to the poles, and temperatures recorded at night in some regions.

As Figure 1 shows, there has been no sustained increase in daily high temperatures since at least 2005, when the National Oceanic and Atmospheric Administration launched its most accurate temperature station network, the Climate Reference Network.[1,2]

Further, the data illustrated in Figure 2 show extended periods of very high temperatures were much more common in the 1930s than they have been in the present decade. Moreover, recent heat wave frequency and intensity remain in line with the historical norm.

Key Takeaways

- In recent decades in the United States, heat waves have been far less frequent and severe than they were in the 1930s.

- The all-time high temperature records set in most states occurred in the first half of the twentieth century.

- The most accurate nationwide temperature station network, implemented in 2005, has shown no sustained, substantial increase in daily high temperatures in the United States since its inception.

Objective data show the all-time high temperature records set in most states occurred in the first half of the twentieth century, decades before anyone was talking about man-caused climate change.[3]

References:

1. U.S. Climate Reference Network, National Oceanic and Atmospheric Administration's (NOAA) National Centers for Environmental Information, accessed August 17, 2021, **https://www.ncdc.noaa.gov/crn**

2. U.S. Climate Reference Network, "Average Surface Temperature, January 2005 to July 2021," ncdc.noaa.gov, National Climatic Data Center, National Oceanic and Atmospheric Administration, last accessed August 14, 2021, **https://bit.ly/3k8jRfD**

3. Patrick Michaels, "Newly Found Weather Records Show 1930s as Being Far Worse than the Present for Extreme Weather," *World Climate Report*, reposted to *Watts Up with That*, wattsupwiththat.com, July 14, 2012, **https://bit.ly/3k8OlIN**

Figure 1. Contiguous U.S. High Temperature Anomalies

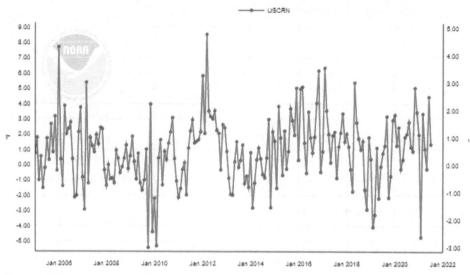

Figure 1. High surface temperature anomalies in the United States, January 2005 to July 2021. *Source*: U.S. Climate Reference Network, "Average Surface Temperature, January 2005 to July 2021," ncdc.noaa.gov, National Climatic Data Center, National Oceanic and Atmospheric Administration, last accessed August 14, 2021, https://bit.ly/3k8jRfD

Figure 2. Heat Wave Index for the Contiguous United States, 1895–2020

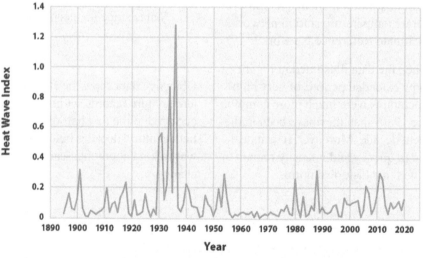

Figure 2. This figure shows the annual values of the U.S. Heat Wave Index, from 1895 to 2020. These data cover the contiguous 48 states. This index defines a heat wave as a period lasting at least four days with an average temperature that would only be expected to occur once every 10 years, based on the historical record. The index value for a given year depends on how often heat waves occur and how widespread they are. *Source*: Graph from Environmental Protection Agency, "Climate Change Indicators: Heat Waves," accessed August 14, 2021, https://www.epa.gov/climate-indicators/ climate-change-indicators-heat-waves#%20. *Data Source*: K. Kunkel, Figure 2.3 in "Weather and Climate Extremes in a Changing Climate," *U.S. Climate Change Science Program: Synthesis and Assessment Product 3.3*, originally published in 2008, updated in 2021, accessed August 14, 2021, www.globalchange.gov/browse/reports/sap-33-weather-and-climate-extremes-changing-climate

U.S. Temperatures

The United States has experienced no significant warming since 2005. The lack of warming is documented by the National Oceanic and Atmospheric Administration's U.S. Climate Reference Network, an extremely accurate network of temperature stations located throughout the United States. Unlike other temperature data, Climate Reference Network data does not require corrective adjustments to account for environmental factors that alter the accuracy of recorded temperatures.

Figure 1 illustrates there has been no significant increase in the number of temperature anomalies since the start of 2006.[1,2] Thus, when climate activists have claimed in recent years that warming has caused various U.S. environmental problems, it's not possible their assessments are accurate, unless it can be shown the U.S. Climate Reference Network data is wrong, and as far as we're aware, no credible scientific agency has attempted to make that claim.

Further, long-term warming in the United States has been modest, at worst. Thermometer readings report current temperatures are no higher today than they were 80 years ago, a reality that has been masked in large part by government agencies that have chosen to adjust temperatures from past decades downward, making it

Key Takeaways

- There has been no significant warming in the United States since 2005.

- Any claimed recent warming and impacts at specific places in the United States are isolated and indicative of random variation, not a long-term warming trend.

- Thermometer readings in the United States suggest current temperatures are similar to those temperatures recorded eight decades ago.

appear as though recent temperatures are comparably much higher than the unadjusted data suggest. (See Figure 2.)

Another factor that has distorted temperature data is the poor placement of temperature stations that are not part of the Climate Reference Network. Many stations' data have been affected by urbanization, resulting in temperature inaccuracies.[3, 4]

The raw, unadjusted data, shown in Figure 2, clearly illustrates recent temperatures are likely the same or nearly the same as they were in the 1930s, and perhaps even lower.[5]

Figure 1. Contiguous U.S. Average Temperature Anomalies

Figure 1. Average surface temperature anomalies in the United States, January 2005 to July 2021. *Source*: U.S. Climate Reference Network, "Average Surface Temperature, January 2005 to July 2021," ncdc.noaa.gov, National Climatic Data Center, National Oceanic and Atmospheric Administration, last accessed August 14, 2021, https://bit.ly/3k8jRfD

Figure 2. USHN Monthly Measured vs. Adjusted Temperatures

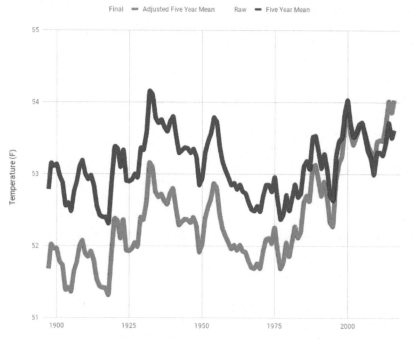

Figure 2. U.S. Historical Climatology Network (USHCN) data. The blue line represents unadjusted thermometer readings, which show temperatures are no higher now than they were 80 years ago. *Source*: Tony Heller, "61% of NOAA USHCN Adjusted Temperature Data Is Now Fake," realclimatescience.com, February 11, 2019, https://realclimatescience.com/2019/02/61-of-noaa-ushcn-adjusted-temperature-data-is-now-fake

References:

1. U.S. Climate Reference Network, National Oceanic and Atmospheric Administration's (NOAA) National Centers for Environmental Information, accessed August 17, 2021, **https://www.ncdc.noaa.gov/crn**

2. U.S. Climate Reference Network, "Average Surface Temperature, January 2005 to July 2021," ncdc.noaa.gov, National Climatic Data Center, National Oceanic and Atmospheric Administration, last accessed August 14, 2021, **https://www.ncdc.noaa. gov/temp-and-precip/national-temperature-index/time-series?datasets%5B%5D=uscr n&parameter=anom-tavg&time_scale=p12&begyear=2005&endyear=2021&month=12**

3. See Anthony Watts, *Is the U.S. Surface Temperature Record Reliable?*, The Heartland Institute and SurfaceStations.org, 2009, **https://www.heartland.org/_template-assets/ documents/publications/SurfaceStations.pdf**

4. See Anthony Watts *et al.*, "New Study of NOAA's U.S. Climate Network Shows a Lower 30-Year Temperature Trend When High Quality Temperature Stations Unperturbed by Urbanization Are Considered," press release, American Geophysical Union, December 16, 2015, displaying parts of a presentation delivered before the American Geophysical Union, **https://web.archive.org/web/20160331214630/https://fallmeeting.agu. org/2015/press-item/new-study-of-noaas-u-s-climate-network-shows-a-lower-30- year-temperature-trend-when-high-quality-temperature-stations-unperturbed-by- urbanization-are-considered**

5. Tony Heller, "61% of NOAA USHCN Adjusted Temperature Data Is Now Fake," realclimatescience.com, February 11, 2019, **https://realclimatescience.com/2019/02/61- of-noaa-ushcn-adjusted-temperature-data-is-now-fake**

U.S. Wildfires

Wildfires, especially in arid parts of the United States, have always been a natural part of the environment, and they likely always will. Global warming did not create wildfires. In fact, wildfires have become less frequent and less severe in recent decades. One of the key contributing factors has been that the United States has experienced fewer droughts in recent decades than in periods throughout the twentieth century.[1]

The U.S. National Interagency Fire Center (NIFC) provides data about U.S. wildfires dating back to 1926. NIFC data show the number of acres burned in recent years has been far less than it was during the early twentieth century. (See Figure 1.) The number of acres burned in modern wildfires is roughly one-fourth to one-fifth of the size of the record values that occurred in the 1930s. At that time, the peak wildfire burn was greater than 52 million acres. From 2010 to 2020, the peaks were typically just 10 million acres or less.[2]

Some climate activists cite a relatively small upward trend, starting in 1983, in the number of acres burned by wildfires as evidence that climate change has been making wildfires considerably worse. However, the data show that trend is minor compared to the much longer historical record. Wildfires burned far more acres, on average, prior to 1950.

Key Takeaways

- Compared to the first half of the twentieth century, the number of wildfires occurring in the United States over the past decade is lower, and the fires have been less severe.

- In years in which there has been an increase in wildfire activity during the past decade, the fires have usually involved substantially fewer acres of burnt land compared to much of the twentieth century.

- Even in the worst wildfire seasons occurring recently, wildfires typically burned one-fifth to half as much land as standard wildfire seasons during the early twentieth century.

- Drought is the key climate factor for wildfires, an important consideration because the United States has experienced relatively few droughts recently.

- Data showing greater numbers of acres lost to wildfires in previous decades were removed from an important database by a government fire agency, likely because the data did not support the claim that wildfires are becoming more frequent.

Even more disturbing, climate activists and several scientists have deleted significant amounts of wildfire data from years prior to the start of the upward trend, making it appear as though the United States is in the midst of a much greater trend than the historical record shows.

In March 2021, NIFC removed wildfire data from years prior to 1983. The stated justification for the decision was that data are allegedly "unreliable," an assertion that should be viewed with great skepticism considering that this supposedly unreliable data had been used in peer-reviewed scientific publications for many decades.

By disappearing all data prior to 1983, which happens to be the lowest point in the dataset for the number of fires, NIFC data now suggest wildfires are getting much worse and that the number of fires is aligned with global temperature. Without a distorted dataset, these dire claims about wildfires would be impossible to make with any degree of credibility. (See Figure 2.)

Figure 1. Wildland Fires: Number of Acres Burned in the United States, 1926–2019

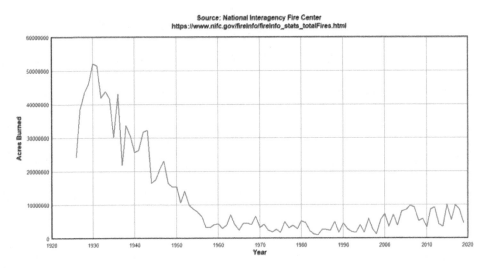

Figure 1. Available wildfire acreage burned, by year, in the United States, 1926 to 2019. This includes data from NIFC prior to the disappearance of data that occurred in 2021. *Source*: Graph by Anthony Watts.

Figure 2. A Comparison of NIFC Datasets, Number of Acres Burned in the United States, 1926–2020 and 1983–2020

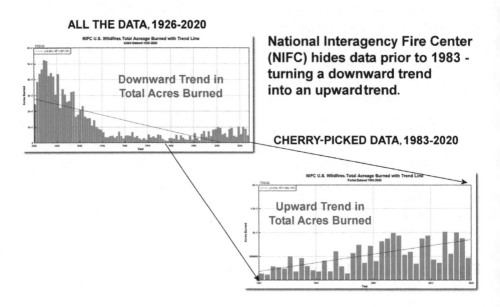

Figure 2. A comparison of NIFC wildfire datasets. It illustrates that when NIFC agreed to remove wildfire data for the years prior to 1983, it provided the public with a distorted view of wildfires. Graphs by Anthony Watts.

References:

1. See *Climate at a Glance*, "Drought," The Heartland Institute, accessed August 15, 2021, **https://climateataglance.com/climate-at-a-glance-drought/**

2. National Interagency Fire Center, "Total Wildfire Acreage Burned by Year in the United States, 1983 to 2020," data last accessed on August 16, 2021, **https://www.nifc.gov/fireInfo/fireInfo_stats_totalFires.html**

Section 4

Humans and Animals

Climate Refugees

For the past 30 years, climate activists have claimed that islands, cities, and even entire nations would spawn millions of refugees, as climate change makes many places inhospitable or uninhabitable. In 1989, for example, a senior U.N. environmental official claimed that "entire nations could be wiped off the face of the Earth by rising sea levels if the global warming trend is not reversed by the year 2000."[1]

Similarly, in 2005, the United Nations claimed, "Rising sea levels ... will create up to 50 million environmental refugees by the end of the decade."[2]

Those predictions proved to be false, along with hundreds of others made by climate change activists. To avoid embarrassment, the United Nations removed the prediction—which we reprint here, as Figure 1—of "50 million environmental refugees" from its website.[3]

As documented in the *Climate at a Glance* article "Islands and Sea-Level Rise" (see page 30), most small islands, including the islands of Tuvalu, are growing in size, not shrinking due to rising sea levels.[4] Further, nearly every nation is benefiting from steadily increasing crop yields, which have improved in part because of recent modest warming periods.[5] And the number of climate-related disasters, as well as the number of victims from those disasters, has been declining over the past 100 years, as seen in Figure 2.[6]

The factors that climate activists claim will soon cause numerous climate refugee crises are not present and, in many cases, are actually becoming less common and/or severe.

Key Takeaways

- The asserted causes of so-called "climate refugees"—increasing crop failures, catastrophic weather events, and islands lost to rising seas—have not materialized.

- Despite much fear-mongering, a majority of the islands some climate activists have predicted would be associated with producing climate refugees due to sea-level rise have had their land mass increase in recent decades, not shrink.

- Nearly all of the nations that are expected to produce climate refugees due to crop failures have benefited in recent years from steadily increasing crop yields.

- The United Nations confirms casualties linked to climate-related natural disasters have declined this century.

Figure 1. U.N. Map Predicting Where 50 Million Climate Change Refugees Will Move

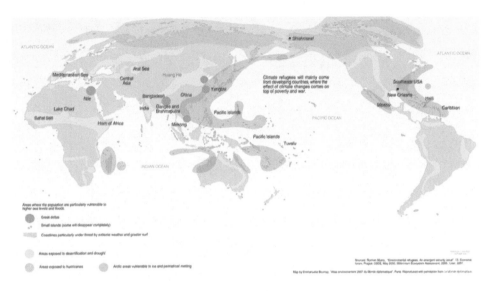

Figure 1. Original map created in 2005 by the United Nations to illustrate where "50 million climate refugees" would move. The map has since been removed from the internet by the United Nations. *Source:* Anthony Watts, "The UN 'Disappears' 50 Million Climate Refugees, then Botches the Disappearing Attempt," *WattsUpWithThat*, April 2011, https://wattsupwiththat.com/2011/04/15/the-un-disappears-50-million-climate-refugees-then-botches-the-disappearing-attempt/

Figure 2. Number of Climate-Related Disasters per Year by Disaster Sub-Group, 2000–2019

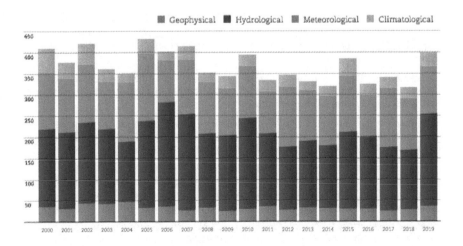

Figure 2. This chart published by the United Nations shows a downward trend in the number of climate-related disasters. *Source:* Nima Yaghmaei *et al.*, *The Human Cost of Disasters: An Overview of the Last 20 Years (2000-2019)*, U.N. Office for Disaster Risk Reduction and Centre for Research on the Epidemiology of Disasters, October 13, 2020, https://www.undrr.org/media/48008/download

References:

1. See Eric Worrall, "30 Year Anniversary of the UN 1989 '10 Years to Save the World' Climate Warning," *WattsUpWithThat*, June 30, 2019, https://wattsupwiththat.com/2019/06/30/30-year-anniversary-of-the-un-1989-10-years-to-save-the-world-climate-warning

2. David Adams, "50 Million Environmental Refugees by End of Decade, UN Warns," *The Guardian* (U.K.), October 12, 2005, https://www.theguardian.com/environment/2005/oct/12/naturaldisasters.climatechange1

3. Anthony Watts, "The UN 'Disappears' 50 Million Climate Refugees, then Botches the Disappearing Attempt," *WattsUpWithThat*, April 2011, https://wattsupwiththat.com/2011/04/15/the-un-disappears-50-million-climate-refugees-then-botches-the-disappearing-attempt

4. The Heartland Institute, "Islands and Sea Level Rise," *Climate at a Glance*, accessed August 15, 2021, https://climateataglance.com/climate-at-a-glance-islands-and-sea-level-rise

5. The Heartland Institute, "Crop Production," *Climate at a Glance*, accessed August 15, 2021, https://climateataglance.com/crop-production

6. The Global Warming Policy Foundation, "UN Disasters Report Is a Huge Blunder and Embarrassment," press release, October 12, 2020, https://www.thegwpf.com/un-disasters-report-is-a-huge-blunder-and-embarrassment

COVID-19's Impact on CO2 Levels

Governments' response to the COVID-19 pandemic caused a worldwide reduction in economic activity, as businesses closed, airlines canceled flights, energy production and consumption fell, and people sheltered in their homes.[1] However, some climate activists celebrated the economic shutdowns, arguing that they created the largest-ever drops in global CO2 emissions.[2]

Climate activists expected this economic downturn to result in reduced energy use and fewer CO2 emissions globally, which did occur. China's CO2 emissions declined by 40 percent. U.S. energy-related CO2 emissions also dropped significantly in 2020. However, the global decline in human emissions did not cause a decline or pause in atmospheric carbon dioxide concentrations.[3,4,5]

University of Alabama climate scientist Roy Spencer studied the effect of the pandemic lockdowns on atmospheric CO2 concentrations and found very little, if any, correlation.[6] Spencer conducted his analysis by removing from his data the effects of the large CO2 cycle that occurs during seasonal plant photosynthesis processes, as well as the average effects from El Nino and La Nina events, which change the rate of ocean outgassing of CO2. The results showed that there was no substantial downturn in global atmospheric CO2 levels, despite reduced CO2 emissions.[6,7,8] (See Figure 1.)

Key Takeaways

- The global economy shrank as a consequence of the lockdowns instituted in response to the COVID-19 pandemic.

- Despite crashing economies and large cutbacks in travel, industry, and energy generation, climate scientists have yet to find a substantial decline in atmospheric CO2 levels.

- The lack of a strong reduction in atmospheric CO2 connected to the energy-use decline linked to the COVID-19 pandemic suggests that climate activists' calls for global energy use reductions would be ineffective in limiting atmospheric CO2 levels. These policies would, however, cause significant economic harm.

NOAA's Earth System Research Laboratories also studied the issue and concluded, "That drop in emissions needs to be large enough to stand out from natural CO2 variability caused by how plants and soils respond to seasonal and annual variations of temperature, humidity, soil moisture, etc. These natural variations are large, and so far, the 'missing' emissions do not stand out."[10]

Clearly, there is no indication that the forced reductions in economic activity and human CO2 emissions had any effect on global CO2 levels, suggesting that natural forces, such as ocean outgassing of CO2, overwhelmed humans' contributions. This further suggests that calls from climate activists to reduce fossil-fuel use, automobile use, airline travel, beef consumption, etc., would likely have little or no impact on atmospheric CO2 concentrations, unless imposed dramatically and over the long term. Of course, that would undoubtedly be accompanied by an equivalent long-term reversal in economic progress and living standards.

Figure 1. Atmospheric CO2 Concentrations

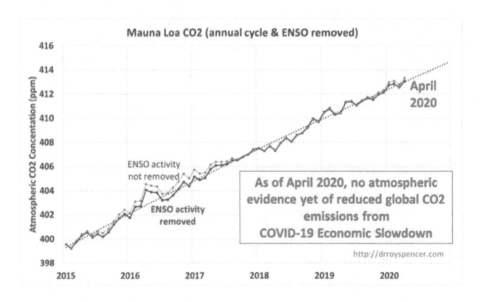

Figure 1. Using a simple method for removing the large seasonal cycle from the Mauna Loa CO2 data, as well as the average effects from El Nino and La Nina events, Spencer analyzed atmospheric CO2 concentrations during the height of the COVID-19 lockdowns and found there was no obvious downturn in global CO2 levels. It is worth noting that *USA Today* conducted a fact check on this issue and found the same result.[9] *Source*: Roy Spencer, "March 2020 CO2 Levels at Mauna Loa Show no Obvious Effect from Global Economic Downturn," drroyspencer.com, April 7, 2020, https://www.drroyspencer.com/2020/04/march-2020-co2-levels-at-mauna-loa-show-no-obvious-effect-from-global-economic-downturn

References:

1. Josh Zumbrun, "Coronavirus-Afflicted Global Economy Is Almost Certainly in Recession," *The Wall Street Journal*, April 14, 2020, **https://www.wsj.com/articles/coronavirus-afflicted-global-economy-is-almost-certainly-in-recession-11586867402**

2. Tobias Hoonhout, "Dem Rep. Told Colleagues Coronavirus Bill Is 'Tremendous Opportunity to Restructure Things to Fit Our Vision,'" *National Review*, March 23, 2020, **https://www.nationalreview.com/news/dem-rep-told-colleagues-coronavirus-bill-is-tremendous-opportunity-to-restructure-things-to-fit-our-vision**

3. Lauren Sommer, "Why China's Air Has Been Cleaner During the Coronavirus Outbreak," National Public Radio, March 4, 2020, **https://www.npr.org/sections/goatsandsoda/2020/03/04/811019032/why-chinas-air-has-been-cleaner-during-the-coronavirus-outbreak**

4. U.S. Energy Information Administration, "Short Term Energy Outlook," May 2020, accessed August 15, 2021, **https://www.eia.gov/outlooks/steo/archives/may20.pdf**

5. NASA, "Seasonal Changes in Carbon Dioxide," *Scientific Visualization Studio*, May 4, 2017, accessed August 15, 2021, **https://svs.gsfc.nasa.gov/4565**

6. Roy Spencer, "Is the COVID-19 Economic Downturn Affecting Atmospheric CO2? Mauna Loa Data Say, Not Yet," drroyspencer.com, March 22, 2020, **https://www.drroyspencer.com/2020/03/is-the-covid-19-economic-downturn-affecting-atmospheric-co2-mauna-loa-data-say-not-yet**

7. Roy Spencer, "Why the Current Economic Slowdown Won't Show Up in the Atmospheric CO2 Record," drroyspencer.com, May 15, 2020, **http://www.drroyspencer.com/2020/05/why-the-current-economic-slowdown-wont-show-up-in-the-atmospheric-co2-record**

8. Roy Spencer, "March 2020 CO2 Levels at Mauna Loa Show no Obvious Effect from Global Economic Downturn," drroyspencer.com, April 7, 2020, **https://www.drroyspencer.com/2020/04/march-2020-co2-levels-at-mauna-loa-show-no-obvious-effect-from-global-economic-downturn**

9. Matthew Brown, "Fact check: The Coronavirus Pandemic Isn't Slowing Climate Change," *USA Today*, May 11, 2020, **https://www.usatoday.com/story/news/factcheck/2020/05/11/fact-check-coronavirus-pandemic-isnt-slowing-climate-change/3090790001/**

10. National Oceanic and Atmospheric Administration, "Can We See a Change in the CO2 Record Because of COVID-19?," NOAA Earth System Research Laboratories, May 2020, **https://www.esrl.noaa.gov/gmd/ccgg/covid2.html**

Livestock and Methane

Climate activists often claim that ranchers, livestock, and meat production are a leading cause of rising greenhouse gas emissions and global warming. However, the U.S. Environmental Protection Agency (EPA) has compiled information on greenhouse gas emissions by source. According to EPA, beef production accounts for 2 percent of U.S. greenhouse gas emissions, while livestock production accounts for less than 4 percent of U.S. greenhouse gas emissions.[1]

By contrast, U.S. agricultural crop production emits more greenhouse gases than total livestock production. This is the case even though the United States leads the world in beef production.[2]

Livestock primarily impact greenhouse gas emissions through methane released when livestock burp or pass gas. Although this is often presented as a serious problem, data show U.S. methane emissions have fallen over the past three decades. According to EPA, methane emissions dropped from 1990 to 2018.[3]

Key Takeaways

- American ranchers and meat consumption have virtually no impact on overall greenhouse gas emissions or climate change.

- EPA reports cattle and beef production account for 2 percent of U.S. greenhouse gas emissions.

- EPA reports all livestock account for less than 4 percent of U.S. greenhouse gas emissions.

References:

1. U.S. Environmental Protection Agency, "Inventory of U.S. Greenhouse Gas Emissions and Sinks," epa.gov, accessed August 15, 2021, **https://www.epa.gov/ghgemissions/inventory-us-greenhouse-gas-emissions-and-sinks**

2. Rob Cook, "Ranking of Countries that Produce the Most Beef (USDA)," Beef2Live.com, citing data from the U.S. Department of Agriculture, August 16, 2021, **https://beef2live.com/story-world-beef-production-ranking-countries-0-106885**

3. U.S. Environmental Protection Agency, "Greenhouse Gas Inventory Data Explorer," accessed August 15, 2021, **https://cfpub.epa.gov/ghgdata/inventoryexplorer**

Figure 1. Greenhouse Gas Emissions by Sector

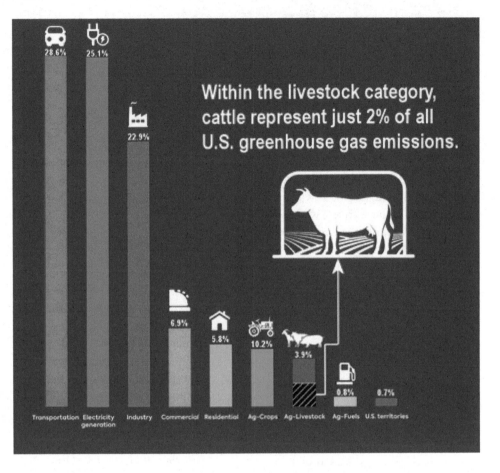

Figure 1. Greenhouse gas emissions by sector in the United States. Note that beef production is less than half of the entire livestock sector, at just 2 percent. *Source*: Data from U.S. Environmental Protection Agency. Graphic by Anthony Watts. Artwork icons in graphic licensed from 123rf.com.

Malaria and Mosquito-Borne Diseases

C laims that higher temperatures will cause more malaria cases and deaths are contradicted by real-world evidence. As the Earth has warmed in recent decades, malaria cases and deaths have declined in nearly all areas of the world. If global warming causes more malaria cases, we certainly should have witnessed additional deaths related to malaria by now.

The World Health Organization (WHO) publishes global estimates of the number of people who die from malaria. Since 2000, the global death toll has been cut in half—from 839,000 deaths in 2000 to 438,000 in 2015—according to a report by WHO.[1]

Africa is the region of the world that is most affected by malaria, with nine out of every 10 malaria victims living in Africa. As shown in Figure 1, Africa is also the region that has achieved the most progress in preventing death from malaria, even as the Earth has modestly warmed.

As detailed in Chapter Four of *Climate Change Reconsidered II: Fossil Fuels*, the vast body of scientific literature refutes climate activists' claim that climate change is likely to exacerbate the spread of mosquito-borne diseases.[2] Further, as seen in Figure 2, Australia, Europe, North America, South America, and the United Kingdom reported zero deaths from

Key Takeaways

- The number of malaria deaths occurring globally has declined in recent decades, not increased, despite modest global warming.

- The death toll for malaria worldwide has been cut in half since 2000.

- There have been no recorded malaria deaths in North America or Europe since 1990, even though malaria deaths were frequent on both continents in the early 1900s.

- If global warming causes an uptick in mosquito-borne diseases, malaria being the most prevalent, the world should have already seen a substantial increase in illnesses and deaths from malaria and other mosquito-borne diseases, not a dramatic decline.

malaria from 1990 through 2017.[3]

Even though media attempts continue to raise a false alarm, peer-reviewed research demonstrates there is simply no link at all between mosquito-borne diseases and a modestly warming world.[4,5]

Figure 1. Global Malaria Deaths by Region of the World

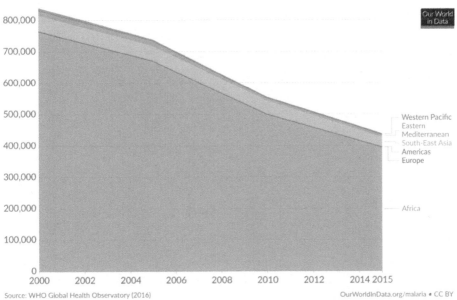

Figure 1. Global Malaria Deaths by Region, 2000–2015. *Source*: Max Roser and Hannah Ritchie, "Malaria," *Our World in Data*, Oxford Martin School, University of Oxford, last updated October 2019, https://ourworldindata.org/malaria#malaria-death-estimates-from-who

Figure 2. Death Rate from Malaria, 2017

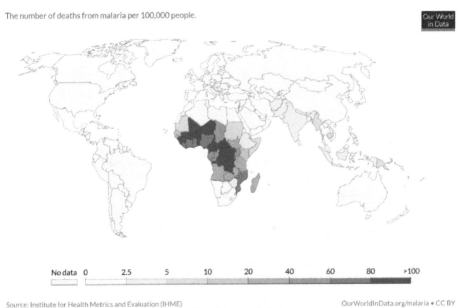

Figure 2. The map visualization shows the age-standardized death rate caused by malaria, measured as the number of deaths per 100,000 individuals. Note that Africa is where the vast majority of cases occur. *Source*: "Death Rates from Malaria, 2017," *Our World in Data*, Oxford Martin School, University of Oxford, accessed August 15, 2021, https://ourworldindata.org/grapher/malaria-death-rates?time=1990

References:

1. Max Roser and Hannah Ritchie, "Malaria," *Our World in Data*, Oxford Martin School, University of Oxford, last updated October 2019, **https://ourworldindata.org/malaria#malaria-death-estimates-from-who**

2. Roger Bezdek, Craig Idso, David Legates, S. Fred Singer, lead authors, *Climate Change Reconsidered II: Fossil Fuels* (Arlington Heights, IL: Nongovernmental International Panel on Climate Change, 2018), ISBN 978-1-934791-59-2, **http://climatechangereconsidered.org/climate-change-reconsidered-ii-fossil-fuels/**

3. "Death Rates from Malaria, 2017," *Our World in Data*, Oxford Martin School, University of Oxford, accessed August 15, 2021, **https://ourworldindata.org/grapher/malaria-death-rates?time=1990**

4. Zoe Corbyn, "Global Warming Wilts Malaria, Transmission of Infectious Parasites Slows with Rising Temperatures, Researchers Find," *Nature*, nature.com, December 21, 2011, **https://www.nature.com/news/global-warming-wilts-malaria-1.9695**

5. H. Sterling Burnett, "NPR Makes False Connection Between Climate Change and Disease," *Climate Realism*, August 28, 2020, **http://climaterealism.com/2020/08/npr-makes-false-connection-between-climate-change-and-disease**

Polar Bears

Climate activists often speculate that even a modest amount of warming would reduce Arctic ice and food availability by so much that it would push polar bears to extinction. The evidence suggests this is false, however. Polar bears evolved hundreds of thousands of years ago and have thrived under much warmer climatic conditions than those that exist today,[1] including during the Mid-Holocene Warm Period, which lasted for 2,000 years and occurred between 5,000 to 7,000 years ago.[2]

After dropping to a low of 10,000 bears in 1950, during the middle of a global cooling period, polar bear numbers have quadrupled to as many as 39,000 today. Further, polar bear experts, such as Susan Crockford, have documented at length how polar bear populations have managed to increase despite a modestly warming world.[3] (See Figure 1.)

Contrary to the many dire claims made by climate activists about polar bears, proof of declining polar bear populations essentially vanishes when all of the available data are considered.[4]

Key Takeaways

- Polar bear populations have increased dramatically during recent decades, despite the modest global warming that has occurred over the same period.

- The estimated polar bear population has nearly quadrupled since 1950, rising from 10,000 bears in 1950 to as many as 39,000 bears today.

- Polar bears evolved between six million years ago and 350,000 years ago, and they survived and even thrived in much warmer climates than what we're seeing today.

Figure 1. Global Polar Bear Population Size Estimates

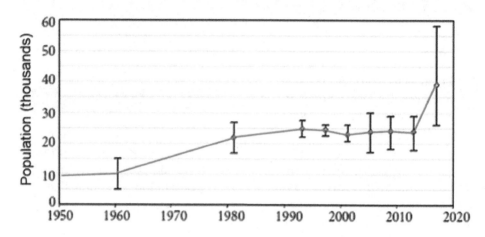

Figure 1. Global polar bear population. *Source*: Susan J. Crockford, *The Polar Bear Catastrophe That Never Happened*, Chapter 10 (London, U.K.: The Global Warming Policy Foundation, 2019).

References:

1. Polar Bears International, "The Evolution of the Polar Bear," polarbearsinternational.org, accessed August 15, 2021, **https://polarbearsinternational.org/polar-bears/name-evolution**

2. National Centers for Environmental Information, "Mid-Holocene Warm Period," National Oceanic and Atmospheric Administration, accessed August 15, 2021, **https://www.ncdc.noaa.gov/global-warming/mid-holocene-warm-period**

3. Susan J. Crockford, *State of the Polar Bear Report 2018*, The Global Warming Policy Foundation, February 2019, accessed August 15, 2021, **https://www.thegwpf.org/content/uploads/2019/02/State-of-the-polar-bear2018.pdf**

4. Susan J. Crockford, *The Polar Bear Catastrophe That Never Happened*, Chapter 10 (London, U.K.: The Global Warming Policy Foundation, 2019).

Section 5
Scientific and Policy Controversies

Climate Sensitivity

Climate sensitivity is a measure of how much the Earth's climate will cool or warm after a change in the climate's system. In scientific circles, climate sensitivity is usually linked to the degree to which temperature will be affected by a doubling in carbon dioxide concentrations in the atmosphere.[1] (See Figure 1.)

Declaring future predictions of global warming as "settled science" requires a fairly precise calculation of future temperatures. However, since climate sensitivity gained scientific visibility more than 40 years ago, scientists and climate models have produced a very broad range of potential future temperature patterns, strongly indicating that no one model can be deemed reliable enough for policymakers to depend upon.[2] Mainstream calculations for a doubling of atmospheric carbon dioxide range from eight-tenths of a degree Celsius warming to almost 6 degrees C of warming by 2100.[3]

If climate scientists don't understand the Earth's atmosphere well enough to nail down a true climate sensitivity estimate for increased carbon dioxide, how can we trust climate model projections of future warming that rely on such an uncertain value?

Further, dire estimates about climate sensitivity have been undercut by real-world data. Climate sensitivity estimates from real-world atmospheric observation data suggest global warming occurring this century is unlikely to exceed 1.5 degrees C.

Key Takeaways

- Predictions that Earth will soon experience substantial global warming rely on the belief that there is a high climate sensitivity to a doubling of carbon dioxide emissions in the atmosphere.

- For decades, scientists have debated the Earth's climate sensitivity, due to the uncertain nature of climate feedback in various models.

- Estimates in peer-reviewed studies range from eight-tenths of a degree C warming to almost 6 degrees C warming by 2100.

- Such a large range means climate model temperature projections are dubious, at best, and cannot provide a reliable estimate that policymakers can depend upon.

- The best evidence indicates climate sensitivity is at the lower end of the estimated range, unlikely to exceed 1.5 degrees C in the twenty-first century.

Figure 1. Factors that Determine Climate Sensitivity

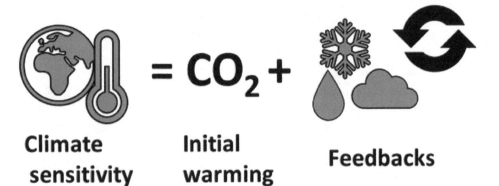

Figure 1. After increasing carbon dioxide levels, there is an initial warming. This warming could be amplified or reduced by the net effect of various feedbacks (weather processes that change the characteristics of the planet). Diagram by Femkemilene from WikiMedia Commons.

References:

1. David L. Chandler, "Explained: Climate Sensitivity," *MIT News*, March 19, 2010, **http://news.mit.edu/2010/explained-climate-sensitivity**

2. *Carbon Dioxide and Climate: A Scientific Assessment*, a report of an Ad Hoc Study Group on Carbon Dioxide and Climate, Climate Research Board of the National Research Council, published by the National Academy of Sciences, July 1979, accessed August 19, 2021, doi:10.17226/12181, **https://web.archive.org/web/20110813231807/http://www.atmos.ucla.edu/~brianpm/download/charney_report.pdf**

3. Schwartz *et. al*, "Earth's Climate Sensitivity: Apparent Inconsistencies in Recent Assessments," *Earth's Future*, Volume 2, Issue 12, November 7, 2014, **https://agupubs.onlinelibrary.wiley.com/doi/full/10.1002/2014EF000273**

4. Richard S. Lindzen and Yong-Sang Choi, "On the Observational Determination of Climate Sensitivity and Its Implications," *Asia-Pacific Journal of Atmospheric Science*, article number 377, August 28, 2011, doi:10.1007/s13143-011-0023-x, **https://link.springer.com/article/10.1007%2Fs13143-011-0023-x**

5. Roy Spencer and William Braswell, "On the Misdiagnosis of Surface Temperature Feedbacks from Variations in Earth's Radiant Energy Balance," *Remote Sensing*, July 25, 2011, doi:10.3390/rs3081603, **http://www.drroyspencer.com/wp-content/uploads/Spencer_Misdiagnos_11.pdf**

6. David Herring, "Are There Positive Benefits from Global Warming?," climate.gov, National Oceanic and Atmospheric Administration, October 29, 2020, **https://www.climate.gov/news-features/climate-qa/are-there-positive-benefits-global-warming**

Carbon Dioxide Taxes

A carbon dioxide tax is a fee imposed on the use of carbon-based fuels, such as coal, oil, and natural gas.[1] Although carbon dioxide taxes have often been touted as "revenue neutral," the purpose of a carbon dioxide tax is to make conventional energy so expensive that people will be coerced into buying wind and solar power, which is already very expensive.

Under a "revenue-neutral" carbon dioxide tax system, energy bills and prices for goods and services throughout the economy increase dramatically because industries and individuals rely increasingly more on expensive wind and solar power. If people were to purchase expensive wind and solar power exclusively, there wouldn't be any carbon dioxide taxes to collect, so no revenue would be collected. When that happens, the carbon dioxide tax becomes revenue neutral for government but inflicts substantial costs on households.

Analysts have repeatedly found that carbon dioxide taxes would raise energy costs, affecting all consumers. For example, researchers Marc Hafstead and Paul Picciano conducted an analysis that estimated carbon dioxide taxes of $50 per metric ton would raise gasoline prices 44 cents per gallon in the United States.[3] (See Figure 1.) The same tax would raise natural gas and coal prices—which account for nearly two-thirds of U.S. electricity generation—by 62 percent and 330 percent, respectively.

Key Takeaways

- A "revenue-neutral" carbon dioxide tax is devised to be revenue neutral for government and only for government.

- A "revenue-neutral" carbon dioxide tax is not revenue neutral for U.S. households.

- Nearly all advocates of a carbon dioxide tax seek to impose the tax in addition to other government restrictions on carbon dioxide, not in place of them.

- "Mainstream" carbon dioxide taxes of $50 per metric ton would likely raise gasoline prices 44 cents per gallon, at minimum.

- "Mainstream" carbon dioxide taxes of $50 per metric ton would likely raise natural gas and coal prices—which account for nearly two-thirds of U.S. electricity generation—62 percent and 330 percent, respectively.

Figure 1. Economic Effects of Carbon Dioxide Taxes

Effects of carbon tax on specific fuels

Select carbon tax | $50 / metric ton CO₂

FOR HOMES AND BUSINESSES

	kg of CO₂	carbon tax	price change per unit
Gasoline	8.89 / gallon (71.3 / BTU)	$0.44 / gallon	■ 22% ($2.00 → $2.44)
Natural gas	53.12 / 1,000 cu. ft. (53.07 / BTU)	$2.66 / 1,000 cu. ft.	■■■ 62% ($4.26 → $6.92)
Propane	5.76 / gallon (63.07 / BTU)	$0.29 / gallon	■■■ 60% ($0.48 → $0.77)
Home heating and diesel fuel (distillate)	10.16 / gallon (73.16 / BTU)	$0.51 / gallon	■ 28% ($1.82 → $2.33)
Residual heating fuel (businesses only)	11.79 / gallon (78.79 / BTU)	$0.59 / gallon	■■ 46% ($1.29 → $1.88)
Kerosene	9.75 / gallon	$0.49 /	■ 28%

Figure 1. The costs added to common home and business fuels after the imposition of a carbon dioxide tax of $50/ton, based on common fuel prices in 2015. *Source:* Marc Hafstead and Paul Picciano, "Calculating Various Fuel Prices under a Carbon Tax," resources.org, November 28, 2017, https://www.resources.org/common-resources/calculating-various-fuel-prices-under-a-carbon-tax

References:

1. Tax Foundation, "What Is a Carbon Tax?," *Tax Basics*, taxfoundation.org, accessed August 15, 2021, **https://taxfoundation.org/tax-basics/carbon-tax**

2. H. Sterling Burnett, "There Is No Revenue-Neutral Carbon-Dioxide Tax," heartland.org, The Heartland Institute, December 4, 2020, **https://www.heartland.org/news-opinion/news/there-is-no-revenue-neutral-carbon-dioxide-tax**

3. Marc Hafstead and Paul Picciano, "Calculating Various Fuel Prices under a Carbon Tax," resources.org, November 28, 2017, **https://www.resources.org/common-resources/calculating-various-fuel-prices-under-a-carbon-tax**

Consensus

S cience is the evaluation of evidence, not a mere vote or show of hands. Throughout the course of human history, there have been many periods during which a majority of scientists have wrongly concluded all sorts of erroneous assertions about the natural world and human beings. It was the scientific method, not consensus, that has allowed our understanding of the universe to expand.

Nevertheless, to the extent people claim a scientific consensus exists about climate change and its potential dangers, there has been only a single scientific organization whose full membership has been polled on climate change issues, the American Meteorological Society (AMS), and the evidence shows AMS members are not deeply concerned about the effects of climate change.

Although surveys of AMS members show two-thirds believe humans are causing a majority of recent warming,[1] the polling results reveal only about 30 percent are very worried about it. And almost as many—28 percent—said they are "not at all worried" or "not very worried." A plurality of respondents (42 percent) reported they are only "somewhat worried," which would seem to indicate they would only support monitoring the scientific evidence and perhaps implementing some modest, cost-effective programs to deal with the effects of climate

Key Takeaways

- Facts and scientific evidence should always trump claims of "consensus."

- A majority of scientists believe the Earth is warming and humans are playing a role, but a strong majority of scientists have said they are not deeply concerned about it.

- The key debate between activists and climate realists is the issue of climate change impacts, not whether humans are causing *some* degree of warming.

- If policymakers do choose to rely on consensus, the only consensus that ought to matter is whether scientists are extremely worried about climate change.

change—not a total or near-total overhaul of the global economy, as so many climate activists have suggested.

Further, it is important to note that 40 percent of AMS members believe climate change impacts have been primarily beneficial or equally mixed between beneficial and harmful, and only half said they expect the impacts to be entirely or primarily harmful over the next 50 years.

Finally, there have been numerous prominent scientists and scientific organizations that have openly and consistently rejected the view that humans are causing a climate change catastrophe, including climate experts with experience working at MIT, Harvard, Columbia, Princeton, and Penn, among many other well-respected academic institutions. Others have served as official state climatologists or have worked for important government agencies, such as NASA and NOAA.[3] Among the many influential scientists who have questioned the causes and/or consequences of the alleged climate change "consensus" are several giants of the scientific world of the past half-century, such as Freeman Dyson, S. Fred Singer, Richard Lindzen, and Will Happer.

References:

1. Center for Climate Change Communication, *A 2016 Survey of American Meteorological Society Members About Climate Change*, George Mason University, March 2016, **https://www.climatechangecommunication.org/wp-content/uploads/2016/04/AMS_Member_Survey_Report_2016.pdf**

2. James Taylor, "NAS Climate Panel Fails the Laugh Test," *Forbes*, May 18, 2011, **https://www.forbes.com/sites/jamestaylor/2011/05/18/nas-climate-panel-fails-the-laugh-test**

3. Craig D. Idso, Robert M. Carter, and S. Fred Singer, *Why Scientists Disagree About Global Warming* (Arlington Heights, IL: The Heartland Institute, 2016), **https://www.heartland.org/_template-assets/documents/Books/Why%20Scientists%20Disagree%20Second%20Edition%20with%20covers.pdf**

Energy Subsidies

Climate activists often assert that fossil-fuel companies benefit from massive federal subsidies, so to level the playing field, wind and solar subsidies are necessary. However, the U.S. Energy Information Administration reports that the wind and solar industries each receive more federal subsidies than all conventional energy sources combined.[1] (See Figure 1.)

Further, indirect subsidies add to the imbalance. Wind and solar businesses often get widespread access to free production on federal lands. They also require lengthy and expensive transmission lines, but typically don't pay for them. Wind and solar also benefit from renewable power mandates, which force consumers in 29 states to purchase a set amount of electricity from "renewable" sources. Wind and solar energy sources further impose extra burdens and costs on baseload conventional energy due to the unpredictability of wind and solar power.

In response to these facts, wind and solar power advocates try to counter—often without documentation—by asserting that conventional energy has *historically* received disproportionate subsidies from the federal government. Even if that were true, two wrongs don't make a right, and consumers should not have to pay higher taxes today to balance out subsidies from, say, the 1950s.

Key Takeaways

- Fossil fuels and conventional energy resources receive relatively few federal subsidies.

- On its own, wind power receives more subsidies than all conventional energy sources combined.

- Similarly, the solar power industry receives more subsidies than all conventional energy sources combined.

Figure 1. Wind and Solar Power Subsidies in Fiscal Years 2010, 2013, and 2016

million 2016 dollars, unless otherwise specified

Year and Support Type	Coal	Refined Coal	Natural Gas and Petroleum Liquids	Nuclear	Renewables	Electricity - Smart Grid and Transmission	Conservation	End Use	Total	Share of Total Subsidies and Support
2010										
Direct Expenditures	48	-	83	69	5,732	4	3,226	6,264	15,427	41%
Tax Expenditures	506	187	2,883	999	8,913	63	3,511	1,055	18,119	48%
Research and Development	320	-	10	177	844	566	704	97	2,718	7%
DOE Loan Guarantee Program	-	-	-	292	296	22	4	1,113	1,728	5%
Total	875	187	2,976	1,537	15,785	655	7,446	8,530	37,992	100%
Share of Total	2%	0%	8%	4%	42%	2%	20%	22%	100%	
2013										
Direct Expenditures	77	-	388	38	8,716	9	872	3,349	13,450	46%
Tax Expenditures	801	10	2,345	1,155	5,683	219	657	2,081	12,951	44%
Research and Development	216	-	64	197	864	887	517	189	2,934	10%
DOE Loan Guarantee Program	-	-	-	-	-	-	-	-	-	-
Total	1,094	10	2,796	1,390	15,264	1,115	2,046	5,619	29,335	100%
Share of Total	4%	0%	10%	5%	52%	4%	7%	19%	100%	
2016										
Direct Expenditures	19	-	111	40	909	11	234	3,391	4,716	31%
Tax Expenditures	906	-	(940)	160	5,316	160	560	2,653	8,816	59%
Research and Development	337	-	56	164	456	49	189	200	1,451	10%
DOE Loan Guarantee Program	-	-	-	-	-	-	-	-	-	-
Total	1,262	-	(773)	365	6,682	220	983	6,244	14,983	100%
Share of Total	8%	-	(5%)	2%	45%	1%	7%	42%	100%	

Notes: Totals may not equal sum of components due to independent rounding. Zero denotes rounding to zero value and a "-" symbol denotes a zero value. Energy-specific tax expenditures associated with renewables were allocated based on preliminary generation data. No hydropower generation was assumed to be eligible for production tax credits (PTC). It was assumed all investment tax credits were claimed by solar power plants. Municipal Solid Waste (MSW) and open-loop biomass generation estimates used to calculate PTCs were halved to represent the value of their PTC credit, relative to geothermal and wind. Generation estimates for 2016 were used to calculate credits associated with the PTC for wind plants that came online in 2006 and later.

Figure 1. This table shows that the wind and solar power industries each receive more subsidies than all conventional energy sources combined. *Source*: U.S. Energy Information Administration, "Direct Federal Financial Interventions and Subsidies in Energy in Fiscal Year 2016," Independent Statistics and Analysis, Tables 3 and 4, April 2018, https://www.eia.gov/analysis/requests/subsidy/pdf/subsidy.pdf

References:

1. U.S. Energy Information Administration, "Direct Federal Financial Interventions and Subsidies in Energy in Fiscal Year 2016," *Independent Statistics and Analysis*, Tables 3 and 4, April 2018, **https://www.eia.gov/analysis/requests/subsidy/pdf/subsidy.pdf**

National Security

E conomic strength is the most important factor in determining a nation's ability to fund and deploy a powerful military over the long term. America's economic might is one of the primary reasons it has, by far, the world's most capable military, even though Russia and Canada are larger in size, geographically, and China and India have far more people.

Affordable energy is the lifeblood of America's economy. Forcing businesses, households, and government agencies to unnecessarily depend on expensive energy sources would reduce economic output and limit United States' ability to fund and deploy a robust military. Thus, climate activism puts U.S. national security at grave risk.

Although climate activists claim global warming is increasing national security "threat multipliers," the truth is, the opposite is happening. Even if one accepts climate activists' dubious claims that weather events like droughts and floods pose a serious threat to U.S. national security interests, or that climate change is causing or will soon cause waves of climate refugees to stream across America's borders, Earth's modest recent warming has actually had a net beneficial impact on extreme weather events and agriculture. For instance, the frequency and severity of droughts, crop failures, weather-related deaths, and wildfires have all

Key Takeaways

- Climate activism, not climate change, poses a significant threat to U.S. national security.

- The economic strength of the United States is the single greatest factor for ensuring the American military remains dominant.

- Proposals to restrict U.S. carbon dioxide emissions would impose expensive, unstable energy sources on Americans that could destroy the U.S. economy.

- Earth's modest recent warming is reducing national security "threat multipliers," such as crop failures and weather-related catastrophes.

declined in recent decades relative to the long-term historical record.[1]

One of the most important examples is global crop production, which has experienced consistent growth in the twenty-first century, in large part due to the presence of higher-than-usual atmospheric carbon dioxide and modest warming trends. Global crop yields have set new records nearly every year, reducing climate-related pressures for people to flee their countries.[2]

Additionally, the United States is one of the world's leading producers of the coal, oil, and natural gas that power the American and global economies.[3] This affords Americans energy security and allows them to bolster allies against the threat of geopolitical energy threats.

By contrast, rare earth minerals are necessary for the construction of wind and solar power equipment. China produces and refines more rare earth minerals than the rest of the world combined.[4] Restricting U.S. conventional energy sources and switching to a wind- and/or solar-based economy would place the United States and its allies at the mercy of the Chinese Communist Party.[5]

References:

1. See various articles on climate-related weather events published by *Climate at a Glance*, The Heartland Institute, climateataglance.com.

2. U.N. Food and Agriculture Organization, "World Food Situation," fao.org, March 12, 2020, **http://www.fao.org/worldfoodsituation/csdb/en**

3. Robert Rapier, "The Ten Countries That Dominate World Fossil Fuel Production," *Forbes*, June 14, 2019, **https://www.forbes.com/sites/rrapier/2019/07/14/ten-countries-that-dominate-fossil-fuel-production**

4. Melissa Pistilli, "10 Top Countries for Rare Earth Metal Production," *Rare Earth Investing News*, March 23, 2021, **https://investingnews.com/daily/resource-investing/critical-metals-investing/rare-earth-investing/rare-earth-metal-production**

5. James Taylor, "Global Warming Energy Restrictions Threaten U.S. National Security," *Policy Brief*, The Heartland Institute, March 2019, **https://www.heartland.org/_template-assets/documents/publications/GlobalWarmingNatSec.pdf**

48334131R00046